THE CHEMICAL HISTORY
OF A CANDLE

Michael Faraday

The Chemical
History of a
CANDLE

ILLUSTRATED BY JEANYEE WONG

Foreword by E. N. da C. Andrade
Biographical introduction by Sir J. Arthur Thomson

NEW YORK: THOMAS Y. CROWELL COMPANY

INTRODUCTION

Michael Faraday

BY PROF. J. ARTHUR THOMSON
MARISCHAL COLLEGE, ABERDEEN

FARADAY'S *Lectures on the Chemical History of a Candle* were delivered to an audience of young people at the Royal Institution in London. They were given more than once, the last occasion being at Christmas, 1860. This seems a very long time ago, but the lectures remain fresh and true. For the man who gave them was a great genius who saw deeply into things and made facts live; and the way in which he coaxed the candle to yield up its secrets is a fine illustration of the way the scientific investigator goes to work.

It is useful to have knowledge about things, but it is still more useful to know how that knowledge has been gained and how it may grow. If someone reads *The Chemical History of a Candle* carefully, and if he puts to a candle of his own the

v

questions Faraday asked of his, he is likely to get an idea of the method by which discoveries are made, and he may be prompted to go on to be a discoverer himself. When Faraday was a boy he was greatly interested in a simple book, Mrs. Marcet's *Conversations on Chemistry,* and he set to work to see if the statements made in the book were true. "I made," he says, "such simple experiments in chemistry as could be defrayed in their expense by a few pence per week." Of course nothing could have kept back a genius like Faraday, but the biographical fact is that an old-fashioned book on chemistry was one of the influences that shaped his life.

Now, what *we* have in *The Chemical History of a Candle* is a book that cannot become old-fashioned; its way of teaching is so true and sure. Many a one who read Faraday's book when a boy has been grateful for a lifetime, for it makes clear the difference between knowledge that can be tested and mere hearsay, between knowledge that is exact and vague opinions, between knowledge that is clear and misty views. We do not mean that there is no other kind of knowledge except this scientific knowledge—Faraday never agreed to that—we mean that science is a verifiable, exact, clear kind of knowledge which is gained by such

ways as Faraday illustrates in this simple *Chemical History of a Candle*. Those who like the book as much as we liked it more than forty years ago will be interested, we think, in a short account of Faraday's life and work, and this is the object of our introduction.

Michael Faraday was born at Newington, then a suburb of London, on September 22, 1791, third child of a journeyman blacksmith, who had come south from Yorkshire. From a common day school Michael passed when he was thirteen to be errand boy to a bookseller. After a year he became an apprentice and began to read some of the books he helped to dust and bind. He became keen for knowledge, and it was a great event when his elder brother, who followed the father's craft, gave him a few shillings to pay for admission to a course of evening lectures on Natural Philosophy. For this meant meeting kindred spirits as well as making a serious start with science.

Another event was that one of the bookseller's customers took the apprentice to hear some Royal Institution lectures by the famous chemist Sir Humphry Davy. The lectures were eagerly mastered. The volume of Faraday's careful notes is still preserved as a precious relic. It is interesting that Faraday heard these lectures in the very room

in Albemarle Street where he afterwards discoursed on "The Chemical History of a Candle," and on hundreds of other subjects.

Going to Sir Humphry Davy's lectures was a turning-point in a curious way; the great chemist got his eye seriously injured in an explosion, and Faraday was somehow or other called in to write letters for him. When this short engagement came to an end, Faraday took "the bold and simple step" (as he called it) of writing to the great man, offering himself as an assistant. In Dr. J. H. Gladstone's *Michael Faraday* (1872) we read that Davy called with the letter on one of his friends, and said, "Pepys, what am I to do? Here is a letter from a young man named Faraday; he has been attending my lectures, and wants me to give him employment at the Royal Institution—*what can I do?*" "Do?" replied Pepys. "Put him to wash bottles: if he is good for anything, he will do it directly; if he refuses, he is good for nothing." "No, no," replied Davy, "we must try him with something better than that." And he did.

So in 1813 Faraday became assistant at the Royal Institution, and there he remained at work with ever-brightening fame for over fifty years. Soon after his appointment he had the interesting experience of traveling in Europe with Sir

Humphry Davy for a year and a half. It was like a college course to Faraday. "But his University was Europe; his professors the master whom he served, and those illustrious men to whom the renown of Davy introduced the travellers." Returning to London, Faraday gave his first lecture and published his first paper, and then for years and years he continued assisting Davy, making chemical experiments, giving scientific advice, superintending laboratories, and discovering new knowledge. In 1821 he married, and brought his bride to rooms in the Royal Institution, where he spent most of the rest of his life.

"Up to 1833 Faraday was bringing the forces of nature in subjection to man on a salary of only £100 per annum, with house, coals, and candles, as the funds of the Institution would not at that time afford more." He got another £100 by and by when an admirer founded for his benefit a Professorship of Chemistry. We wish to explain how Faraday lived in comfort and peace of mind when he was receiving so small an income, for the answer contains one of the side-lessons of his life. The fact is that he earned money readily by making chemical analyses for manufacturers and others, and in 1830 his gains from this source amounted to £1,000; next year they were still

more; and they might have increased enormously without anything but credit. But in 1831 Faraday made one of his great discoveries as to the relationship between electricity and magnetism, and he determined to stop money-making and give his whole thought to nature's secrets. Next year, we read, his outside earnings were reduced to £155 9s., and during no subsequent year did they amount to as much. It was quite characteristic of the man that he would not allow himself to be distracted from his high calling of discoverer.

"For year after year the life of Faraday afforded no adventure and little variety, only an ever-growing skill in his favourite pursuits, higher and higher success, and ever-widening fame." But we must not think of him as forever like a stretched bow. He was fond of young folks and of good company; he enjoyed a country ramble and simple house-games; he often went with his wife and niece to the Zoological Gardens or to the theater. He enjoyed his life to the full, and the Sundays not least, for he was a deeply religious man. When his working days were over the Queen offered him (in 1858) a pretty little house at Hampton Court, and it was in quietness there that he spent the evening of his life. He died on August 25, 1867,

one of the most distinguished of scientific investigators. "Altogether it appears that he was decorated with ninety-five titles and marks of merit, including the blue ribbon of science, for in 1844 he was chosen one of the eight foreign associates of the French Academy." For some reason he could never be induced to accept the highest British scientific honors, the presidentships of the Royal Society of London and of the British Association.

Faraday seems to have been lithe of body, very alert and buoyant, with gleaming kindly eyes, and a radiating vitality. In lecturing he was carried away by his subject, and he carried his audience with him in irresistible enthusiasm. There is little use in trying to describe his mind, for he was by himself—a genius. He had, one may say, an unusual power of clear penetrating insight, which includes imagination. Without being trained in mathematics, he had the mathematician's vision. He had great ingenuity in devising experiments, and much of his thinking seems to have been an intensely rapid experimenting inside his head. When he got hold of a clue he followed it up with doggedness, but also with extraordinary quickness. Experts have pointed with astonishment to the shortness of the time that often elapsed between

Faraday's statement of a problem and his discovery of the answer. Speaking of his own work, Faraday said that he always needed to *see* things for himself before he gripped them in his mind. Even when he saw others make some new experiment he did not seem satisfied until he had repeated it himself. He was what is sometimes called "eye-minded." As he said himself: "I was never able to make a fact my own without *seeing* it."

Faraday's mind must have been a very wonderful activity, but he never spoke of his work as magical. To those who would learn he gives simple advice from his own experience. He tells us to get into the "habit of forming clear and precise ideas" and of expressing them in "clear and definite language." Clearness meant everything to Faraday. He tells us to balance one clear idea against another, not to hurry to a decision, not to allow our wishes to tamper with our thoughts, to be sure of facts but doubtful of theories. "The man who is certain he is right is almost sure to be wrong." "We may be *sure* of facts, but our interpretation of facts we should doubt." And another of his sentences runs: "For my part, I think that as facts are the foundation of science, however they may be interpreted, so they are valuable, and often

more so than the interpretations founded upon them." This reminds us of the interjection with which a great Scottish theologian, Dr. Chalmers, used to stop wordy arguments: "Give us a fact, man; give us a fact."

It may seem a little difficult at first sight, but there is something so very fine about a passage Faraday wrote when he was young, that we venture to quote it here. "The philosopher should be a man willing to listen to every suggestion, but determined to judge for himself. He should not be biassed by appearances, have no favourite hypothesis, be of no school, and in doctrine have no master. He should not be a respecter of persons, but of things. Truth should be his primary object. If to these qualities be added industry, he may indeed hope to walk within the veil of the temple of Nature." Faraday lived true to his youthful vision, and he is one of the Immortals. In a very clearly-written book, *Faraday as Discoverer* (1868), Professor Tyndall wrote: "Taking him for all and all, I think it will be conceded that Michael Faraday was the greatest experimental philosopher the world has ever seen; and I will add the opinion, that the progress of future research will tend, not to dim or to diminish, but to en-

hance and glorify the labours of this mighty investigator." We believe that the leading chemists and electricians of today would agree with Professor Tyndall's tribute.

It is interesting to get some details about his everyday ways in his laboratory, and some of them may be of use to us. He was, for instance, extraordinarily neat and tidy, insisting on having a place for everything and on putting back everything he used into its place. In making an experiment he did not like to have things about that were not really needed and he was careful not to waste any energy. Like many very busy men, though not all, he was almost finicking in his orderliness. Perhaps this had something to do with his habit of always picturing things in his head. Disorder was like a discord.

Faraday had great skill with his hands, but it was characteristic of him that he always sought out the simplest possible appliances. Dr. Gladstone tells how Faraday went out with some others one night in the English Channel to study the lights of different lightships; the others had brought their best light-measures or photometers; but the prince of investigators produced a lady's black shawl-pin and showed that it served admirably. In another case, "Steaming up the Thames one

July day in a penny [fare] boat, he was struck with the offensiveness of the water. He tore some white cards into pieces, wetted them so as to make them sink easily, and dropped them into the river at each pier they came to. Their sudden disappearance from sight, though the sun was shining brightly, was proof enough of the impurity of the stream; and he wrote a letter to the *Times* describing his observations, and calling attention to the dangerous state of the river." Dr. Gladstone recalls *Punch*'s cartoon the following week which represented Professor Faraday holding his nose, and presenting his *card* to Father Thames, who rises out of the unsavory water. Faraday was one of the early advocates of more study of science in schools, but his recommendation that the appliances used should be kept very simple has been often forgotten.

It is not possible to make clear in a short time or without much study the great discoveries that Faraday made, but we wish to say three simple things. (1) There is a Greek fable about an "old man of the sea," called Proteus, who looked after Neptune's flocks of seals, and had the power of revealing the future to those who could catch him. But he was unwilling to prophesy and very difficult to catch, for he could change from shape to

shape: at one time a whirlwind and at another time a flame, at one time a stream and at another time a dragon. Now, Dr. Gladstone tells us, in the book we have already mentioned, that the favorite thought of Faraday seems to have been that the various forces of nature were like the changing forms of a Proteus. In other words, Faraday greatly advanced the truth of the "transformations of energies," that the different kinds of power in the world change from form to form. Motion gives rise to heat and heat gives rise to light, and so the changes go. Nothing is ever lost, but the form changes. Especially important was Faraday's work on the relationship of electricity and magnetism, and on the relationship between these and light.

(2) Faraday was the first to clear up what is called the induction of electrical currents—the fact that if an electrified body is brought near another body, with the invisible barrier of air between, the electrical state of the second body is changed. From this discovery a multitude of important consequences have flowed.

(3) Always seeking to break down barriers and disclose the one-ness of things, Faraday was one of the pioneers in condensing gases into liquid and even into solid form, and this discovery also has

born much fruit. But we must be content with saying that few men of science have to their credit so many discoveries of the first rank of importance as Faraday has.

The great value of Faraday's work was in theoretical discovery, rather than in practical invention. He was more concerned with finding out what is true than with making what is useful. But it was in the sunlight of Faraday's theoretical discoveries that many great practical inventions, like telegraphy, electric light, and radio messages, blossomed. And it is very important that everyone should understand that *all* the ingenious practical inventions that have made modern life so different from that of past ages depend on theoretical discoveries made by patient experimenting and hard thinking. What has seemed at the time to impatient people like a waste of brains has often turned out to be of the highest practical importance.

We do not mean, however, that Faraday, the discoverer, held himself aloof from practical applications. On the contrary, he touched many of them with his genius—India rubber, alloys of steel, patent locks, lamps, optical glass, electroplating, mirrors, ventilation, artificial rubies, benzene, and a score of devices in which electromag-

netism is utilized. But we have to remember that what claimed Faraday's full strength was discovering the secrets of nature, not using them. He liked to be called a "philosopher."

His character was marked by great kindliness, a genuine respect and love for his fellow men. Yet he did not suffer fools gladly and he was quick to take fire if he detected what seemed to him any lack of respect for truth or justice or the dignity of science. He had a joyous disposition and radiated good cheer. He seemed to get very close to nature, and no doubt the depth of his knowledge made storms and sunsets, in which he delighted, more full of meaning to him than to ordinary men. He was not the cold man of science, for although he never allowed feeling to influence his scientific thinking, he could not conceal his enthusiasm in discovery or even in observation. He danced round the moving arches of light caused by an electric discharge in vacuum tubes, crying, "Oh, to live always in it." In a tremendous storm he was detected rubbing his hands with delight because he had seen the lightning strike the church tower. "A new fact," Dr. Gladstone tells us, "seemed to charge him with an energy that gleamed from his eyes and quivered through his limbs."

Yet along with these high qualities went more ordinary ones, such as patience and pertinacity. We like this little story: "Arranging some apparatus one day with a philosophical instrument maker, he let fall on the floor a small piece of glass: he made several ineffectual attempts to pick it up. 'Never mind,' said his companion, 'it is not worth the trouble.' 'Well, but, Murray, I don't like to be beaten by something that I have once tried to do.'" We could not end our introduction on a firmer note than this, but there is another that is finer. According to Professor Tyndall, Faraday was "a man of excitable and fiery nature; but through high self-discipline he had converted the fire into a central glow and motive power of life, instead of permitting it to waste itself in useless passion." He had a good nature to start with and by ruling his spirit he made it better.

Coming back to chemistry, let us remember a favorite experiment of Faraday's, which, as Professor Tyndall says, was representative of the man himself. "He loved to show that water in crystallising excluded all foreign ingredients, however intimately they might be mixed with it. Out of acids, alkalis, or saline solutions, the crystal came sweet and pure. By some such natural process in

the formation of this man, beauty and nobleness coalesced, to the exclusion of everything vulgar and low. He did not learn his gentleness in the world, for he withdrew himself from its culture; and still this land of England contained no truer gentleman than he."

FOREWORD

Michael Faraday
and the Christmas Lectures

BY

PROF. E. N. DA C. ANDRADE, D.SC., PH.D., LL.D., F.R.S.

THE Royal Institution, where Faraday was to carry out his famous experimental researches, was founded in 1799 by Benjamin Thompson, Count Rumford. Thompson was born in Massachusetts, but in 1776, as a young man, he left his native land for England, where he had a very successful career and was knighted. Later he went to Bavaria, where he was made Count Rumford (the name by which he is generally known) for his outstanding achievements as a soldier and as an administrator. He was a remarkable character, who carried out scientific work on heat that gave him a sure place in the history of science. The Royal Society of London still awards a Rumford medal every year.

Rumford was a great man for reform and inno-
vations, and the Royal Institution, established soon
after his return to England from Bavaria, was
originally intended to serve as a general center of
scientific instruction, particularly concerned with
practical applications. It had a school for mechan-
ics and other features designed for the benefit of
the technical working classes. But by the time that
Faraday first entered its doors the Institution was
mainly a center for lectures and the seat of the
laboratory where Humphry Davy was carrying
out his researches. The lectures were on all kinds
of subjects, a tradition that still prevails: for in-
stance Samuel Taylor Coleridge, the poet who
wrote *The Ancient Mariner,* lectured on various
aspects of literature, and Edwin Landseer, the
painter, on engraving. Davy was a brilliant orator
and his lectures, which he illustrated with striking
experiments, drew large and fashionable audiences
to the lecture rooms on Albemarle Street in
London.

Davy's lectures fascinated Faraday and deter-
mined him to devote himself to science, if he could
get the opportunity. He made full notes of the
lectures, which he copied out neatly in a quarto
volume, and then wrote to Sir Humphry to ask
him if he could find him some position, sending

him these notes as a proof of his earnestness. Faraday wrote of the subsequent interview, at which Davy offered him the post of laboratory assistant: "At the same time that he thus gratified my desires as to scientific employment, he still advised me not to give up the prospects I had before me, telling me that Science was a harsh mistress, and in a pecuniary point of view but poorly rewarding those who devoted themselves to her service. He smiled at my notion of the superior moral feelings of philosophic men, and said he would leave me to the experience of a few years to set me right on that matter."

It should be noted that what we now call science, and in particular physics, was generally termed natural philosophy in those days, and at most of the Scottish universities the department of physics is still called the department of natural philosophy. By "philosophic men," then, Davy meant men of science. Faraday was accustomed to use the words in the same sense, as when in his first lecture on *The Chemical History of a Candle* he says, as you will find, "We come here to be philosophers . . ." and again "without which you would not be able fully to understand the philosophy of it."

It was in March 1813 that Faraday entered the

service of the Royal Institution, where two rooms were put at his disposal for residence, and he subsequently lived there all his active life and carried out there the investigations which earned for him the name of "The prince of experimenters." He soon began original research, at first mainly in chemistry; and by 1825, the year in which he discovered benzene, he was already famous for his work on electricity and magnetism and for having liquefied the gas chlorine. In that year he was made Director of the Laboratory of the Royal Institution and started the famous series of lectures, known as the Friday Evening Discourses, which endures to this day. They are not always on scientific subjects, but scientific lectures illustrated by experiments have always been prominent.

As an experimental lecturer Faraday was supreme. He took the greatest trouble in devising the experiments and in making sure that they would be successful and seen by everyone. His personality, too, had an extraordinary influence. Shortly after his death Lady Pollock, who knew him well, wrote of him: "He was completely master of the situation; he had his audiences at his command, as he had himself and all his belongings; he had nothing to fret him, and he could

give his eloquence full sway. It was an irresistible eloquence, which compelled attention and insisted upon sympathy. . . . A pleasant vein of humour accompanied his ardent imagination, and occasionally, not too often, relieved the tension. . . . He never suffered an experiment to lead him away from his theme. Every touch of his hand was a true illustration of his argument." The following notes for lecturing were found among Faraday's papers:

"Never to repeat a phrase.

"Never to go back to amend.

"If at a loss for a word, not to ch-ch-ch or eh-eh-eh, but to stop and wait for it. It soon comes, and the bad habits are broken, and fluency soon acquired."

Faraday, although married, was childless, but he was a great lover of children and was always on the friendliest terms with them. In 1826 he started a course of lectures for children delivered round about Christmas time, or, in the official words, a *Christmas Course of Lectures Adapted to a Juvenile Auditory.* Since then the series has continued unbroken to the present day, except for a period during the last World War, when London was much exposed to attack from the air. The first course of Christmas Lectures, as they are always

called for short, was delivered by a Mr. J. Wallis,
not a famous name, but Faraday himself gave the
second course in 1827-1828 (two years have to
be specified, because the lectures always start at
the end of one year and go on into the next), on
Chemistry. Altogether he gave the Christmas lec-
tures nineteen times; in the period from 1851-
1852 to 1860-1861 he gave them every year. These
lectures of Faraday's were in the highest degree
successful in their object, to interest the young in
the principles of science in an entertaining way
rather than merely to amuse them with sensational
and topical oddments of scientific information or
to instruct them in textbook knowledge as in a
schoolroom.

In 1856 Faraday gave a Christmas Lecture on
Attractive Forces. Lady Owen writes of it: "Fara-
day explained the magnet and strength of attrac-
tions. He made us all laugh heartily; and when he
threw a coalscuttle full of coals, a poker, and a
pair of tongs at the great magnet, and they stuck
there, the theatre echoed with shouts of laughter."

Perhaps young people were more easily amused
then than now, but they instantly recognized a
kindred spirit. Reading these impressions of those
who heard him helps us to realize how the lectures
on the candle were delivered, and reading the

lectures shows us what a wealth of fundamental scientific information Faraday could convey in a spirit of good fun and simple enthusiasm.

Two of Faraday's series of Christmas Lectures came out in print. The first book to appear bore the title *A Course of Six Lectures on the Various Forces of Matter and Their Relations to Each Other* and contained the lectures which were given in 1859-1860. The little volume was not written by Faraday. We are told in the preface by William Crookes, who edited it, that the lectures "are printed as they were spoken, *verbatim et literatim*. A careful and skilful reporter took them down, and the manuscript, as deciphered from his notes, was subsequently most carefully corrected by the Editor as regards any scientific points which were not clear to the short-hand writer; hence all that is different arises solely from the impossibility, alas! of conveying the manner as well as the matter of the Lecturer."

There can be no doubt that this applies also to the second book of Christmas Lectures, which appeared in the following year and was *The Chemical History of a Candle,* as reprinted in the present book. It is likewise "Edited by William Crookes," but he does not again tell of how the book was made. In his first preface to the first

edition Crookes pays his tribute to Faraday as a lecturer: "The pleasure which all derive from the expositions of Faraday is of a somewhat different kind to that produced by any other philosopher whose lectures we have ever attended. It is partially derived from his extreme dexterity as an operator. With him we have no chance of apologies for an unsuccessful experiment, no hanging fire in the midst of a series of brilliant demonstrations, producing that depressing tendency akin to the pain felt by an audience at a false note from a vocalist. All is a sparkling stream of eloquence and experimental illustration. We defy a chemist who loves his science, no matter how often he may himself have repeated an experiment, to feel uninterested when seeing it done by Faraday."

In the same year, 1861, that *The Chemical History of a Candle* was first published, William Crookes himself attained fame as the discoverer of a new element, thallium, and later, by a series of remarkable discoveries in chemistry and physics, he became one of the greatest men of science of his time.

The lectures on *The Chemical History of a Candle* were a favorite series with Faraday. He delivered them twice, once in 1848-1849 and once in 1860-1861, the latter occasion being the last

Christmas Lectures that he gave, only shortly before his final retirement and six years before his death. The first words of the first lecture tell of the interest that the subject held for him and how he would like to return to it almost every year. Any man of science today, reading the book, must be struck by the variety of fundamental scientific lessons that Faraday smoothly and naturally draws from this rod of wax with its plaited wick, which might seem a most unpromising subject for six lectures, especially if difficult detail is to be avoided. What profound mastery is required to attain this persuasive simplicity!

Faraday's successor at the Royal Institution, John Tyndall, was also a magnificent lecturer, who followed the traditions of his great predecessor in the experimental art. When in 1872 he went to the United States for a tour of the great cities he took with him not only abundant apparatus for six lectures on light, but also two assistants. These lectures were an outstanding success, in spite of his "strong English accent," to which the newspapers referred. The sensation that they caused is indicated by the fact that the free tickets issued for his lecture in the hall of the Lowell Institute in Boston had a market value of four or five dollars—and a dollar meant a good deal in those days.

The profits of his lecture tour, which were large, he left as a gift to form a trust fund that was used to found Tyndall Fellowships at Harvard, Columbia, and the University of Pennsylvania. At the Royal Institution he gave the Christmas Lectures twelve times, being second only to Faraday in number as well as in excellence.

After Tyndall came Sir James Dewar, who proved a worthy successor both as a great discoverer and as a brilliant experimental lecturer. He gave the Christmas Lectures nine times, one of his most successful courses bearing the title *A Soap Bubble*, which sounds as unpromising a subject for six lectures as does a candle. But scientifically, soap bubbles are no trifle.

Sir William Bragg, the famous physicist who followed Dewar at the Institution, was another of the great Christmas Lecturers and gave four different series, under the titles *Sound; Concerning the Nature of Things* (a title taken from the great Latin poem of Lucretius, *De Rerum Natura*); *Old Trades and New Knowledge;* and *The Universe of Light*. Each of the series appeared as a very successful book, which conveys some of the charm of the lecturer.

The present writer may, perhaps, be permitted the vanity of recording that he gave the Christmas

Lectures three times, being the only man now living who has delivered them more than once.

Astronomy used to be a favorite subject for Christmas Lectures; and, although it does not lend itself much to experiment, it is, of course, eminently suited to be illustrated by slides showing apparatus and photographs of the heavens. The astronomer Sir Robert Ball, a genial Irishman, was particularly popular as a lecturer on such topics and gave the Christmas Lectures five times. Another, who delivered the Christmas Lectures four times, was the Oxford astronomer H. H. Turner, whose book *A Voyage in Space* is founded on the 1913-1914 series. Sir David Gill and Sir James Jeans are other famous men who each delivered a series of Christmas Lectures on astronomical topics. Jeans's book *Through Space and Time* embodied these lectures. The last astronomer to deliver the Lectures was Sir Harold Spencer Jones, until lately Astronomer Royal, who gave a series entitled *Astronomy in Our Daily Life,* in 1944-1945.

The Christmas Lectures are today as much a feature of the Royal Institution as of old. They still start at 3:00 P.M.: there are still the traditional six to the course, beginning on the first Tuesday, Thursday, or Saturday after December

26, and continuing on those days. They are still emphatically for the young. Their elders are welcome to come but are not admitted to the first six rows of seats and are, in general, encouraged to keep in the background. The tradition of inviting one celebrated man of science to give the Christmas Lectures a number of times has passed. Perhaps the old tradition of a simple general theme, of presenting basic scientific conceptions in an unconventional way, as Faraday did here, is passing too, in favor of greater attention to the marvels of modern applied science. There is a tendency today to have as lecturer one who is connected with a great scientific corporation, which, of course, insures a wonderful and impressive display of scientific products and things pertaining to the machines and methods that make them, arranged by an expert staff. This is perhaps natural, with the growing sophistication of the young and with a growing desire to know more of the mysteries of modern technology and processes of all kinds, rather than to hear of the less sensational principles of science. But the old spirit of a scientific Christmas festival for the boys and girls of England continues and will, no doubt, continue long.

CONTENTS

LECTURE I

A Candle: Sources of the Flame

I PROPOSE to bring before you, in the course of these lectures, the Chemical History of a Candle. There is no better, there is no more open door by which you can enter into the study of natural philosophy than by considering the physical phenomena of a candle. There is not a law under which any part of this universe is governed which does not come into play, and is not touched upon, in these phenomena. I trust, therefore, I shall not disappoint you in choosing this for my subject rather than any newer topic, which could not be better, were it even so good.

And now I must first tell you of what candles are made. Some are great curiosities. There is, for example, a very curious substance taken out of some of the bogs in Ireland, called candlewood— a hard, strong, excellent wood, which burns so well that where it is found they make splinters of it, and torches, since it burns like a candle, and gives a very good light indeed. And in this wood we have one of the most beautiful illustrations of the general nature of a candle that I can possibly give. The fuel provided, the means of bringing that fuel to the place of chemical action, the regular and gradual supply of air to that place of action—heat and light—all produced by a little piece of wood of this kind, forming, in fact, a natural candle.

But we must speak of candles as they are in commerce. Here are a couple of candles commonly called dips. They are made of lengths of cotton cut off, hung up by a loop, dipped into melted tallow, taken out again and cooled, then redipped until there is an accumulation of tallow round the cotton. Very small dips were used by the miners in coal mines. In olden times the miner had to find his own candles; and it was supposed that a small candle would not so soon set fire to the firedamp in the coal mines as a large one; and for that reason, as

well as for economy's sake, he had candles made of this sort—20, 30, 40, or 60 to the pound. They have been replaced since then by the steel-mill, and then by the Davy lamp, and other safety lamps of various kinds.

The Davy lamp (A) consists of a common oil lamp (B) having a wire to raise or lower the wick without the need to remove the wire gauze. A platinum filament (C) winds around the wick and would glow should the light go out in a dangerous situation.

And there is the suet—the fat of the ox— Russian tallow, I believe, employed in the manufacture of these dips, which Gay Lussac, or someone who entrusted him with his knowledge, converted into that beautiful substance, stearin. A candle, you know, is not now a greasy thing like an ordinary tallow candle, but a clean thing, and you

may almost scrape off and pulverize the drops which fall from it without soiling anything. This is the process he adopted:[1] the fat or tallow is first boiled with quicklime, and made into a soap, and then the soap is decomposed by sulphuric acid, which takes away the lime, and leaves the fat re-arranged as stearic acid, whilst a quantity of glycerin is produced at the same time. Glycerin—absolutely a sugar, or a substance similar to sugar—comes out of the tallow in this chemical change. The oil is then pressed out of it. The impurities are carried out by the oily part as the pressure goes on increasing, and at last you have left that substance which is melted, and cast into candles.

Then here is a sperm candle, which comes from the purified oil of the spermaceti whale. Here also are yellow beeswax and refined beeswax, from which candles are made. Here, too, is that curious substance called paraffin, and some paraffin candles made of paraffin obtained from the bogs of Ireland.

And how are these candles made? I have told you about dips, and I will show you how molds are made. Let us imagine any of these candles to be made of materials which can be cast. "Cast!" you say. "Why, a candle is a thing that melts; and surely if you can melt it, you can cast it." Not

so. It is wonderful, in the progress of manufacture, and in the consideration of the means best fitted to produce the required result, how things turn up which one would not expect beforehand. Candles cannot always be cast. A wax candle can never be cast. It is made by a particular process, which I can illustrate in a minute or two; but I must not spend much time on it. Wax is a thing which, burning so well, and melting so easily in a candle, cannot be cast. However, let us take a material that can be cast. Here is a frame, with a number of molds fastened in it. The first thing to be done is to put a wick through them. Here is one—a plaited wick, which does not require snuffing[2]—supported by a little wire. It goes to the bottom, where it is pegged in—the little peg holding the cotton tight, and stopping the aperture, so that nothing fluid shall run out. At the upper part there is a little bar placed across, which stretches the cotton and holds it in the mold. The tallow is then melted, and the molds are filled. After a certain time, when the molds are cool, the excess of tallow is poured off at one corner, and then cleaned off altogether, and the ends of the wick cut away. The candles alone then remain in the mold, and you have only to upset them when out they tumble, for the candles are made in the form of cones,

being narrower at the top than at the bottom; so that what with their form and their own shrinking, they only need a little shaking, and out they fall. In the same way are made these candles of stearin and of paraffin.

It is a curious thing to see how wax candles are made. A lot of cottons are hung upon frames and covered with metal tags at the ends to keep the wax from covering the cotton in those places. These are carried to a heater, where the wax is melted. The frames can turn round; and as they turn, a man takes a vessel of wax and pours it first down one, and then the next, and the next, and so on. When he has gone once round, if it is sufficiently cool, he gives the first a second coat, and so on until they are all of the required thickness. When they have been thus clothed, or fed, or made up to that thickness, they are taken off, and placed elsewhere. They are then taken down, and well rolled upon a fine stone slab, and the conical top is molded by properly shaped tubes, and the bottoms cut off and trimmed. This is done so beautifully that they can make candles in this way weighing exactly four, or six, to the pound, or any number they please.

Now, as to the light of the candle. We will light one or two, and set them at work in the perform-

In an oil lamp, the wick is placed in a vessel of oil. When the top of the wick is lighted, the part above the oil will continue to burn.

ance of their proper functions. You observe a candle is a very different thing from a lamp. With a lamp you take a little oil, fill your vessel, put in a little moss or some cotton prepared by artificial means, and then light the top of the wick. When the flame runs down the cotton to the oil, it gets extinguished, but it goes on burning in the part above. Now, I have no doubt you will ask, how is it that the oil, which will not burn of itself, gets up to the top of the cotton, where it will burn? We shall presently examine that; but there is a much more wonderful thing about the burning of a candle than this. You have here a solid substance with no vessel to contain it; and how is it that this solid substance can get up to the place where the flame is? How is it that this solid gets there, it not being a fluid? or, when it is made a fluid, then how is it that it keeps together? This is a wonderful thing about a candle.

You see, then, in the first instance, that after

the candle has been burning for a while a beautiful cup is formed. As the air comes to the candle it moves upwards by the force of the current which the heat of the candle produces, and it so cools all the sides of the wax, tallow, or fuel, as to keep the edge much cooler than the part within; the part within melts by the flame that runs down the wick as far as it can go before it is extinguished, but the part on the outside does not melt. If I made a current in one direction, my cup would be lopsided, and the fluid would consequently run over, for the same force of gravity which holds worlds together holds this fluid in a horizontal position, and if the cup be not horizontal, of course the fluid will run away in guttering. You see, therefore, that the cup is formed by this beauti-

An ascending current of air, produced by the heat of the candle, keeps the outside edge cool, forming a cup for the melted wax.

fully regular ascending current of air playing upon all sides, which keeps the exterior of the candle cool.

No fuel would serve for a candle which has not the property of giving this cup, except such fuel as the Irish bogwood, where the material itself is like a sponge, and holds its own fuel. You see now why you would have such a bad result if you were to burn these beautiful candles which are irregular, intermittent in their shape, and cannot therefore have that nicely formed edge to the cup which is the great beauty in a candle. I hope you will now see that the perfection of a process—that is, its utility—is the better point of beauty about it. It is not the best-looking thing, but the best-acting thing, which is the most advantageous to us. An irregular candle is a bad-burning one. There will be a guttering round about it because of the irregularity of the stream of air and the badness of the cup which is formed thereby.

You may see some pretty examples (and I trust you will notice these instances) of the action of the ascending current when you have a little gutter run down the side of a candle, making it thicker than it is elsewhere. As the candle goes on burning, that keeps its place and forms a little pillar sticking up by the side, because, as it rises higher

above the rest of the wax or fuel, the air gets better round it, and it is more cooled and better able to resist the action of the heat at a little distance. Now, the greatest mistakes and faults with regard to candles, as in many other things, often bring with them instruction which we should not receive if they had not occurred. We come here to be philosophers; and I hope you will always remember that whenever a result happens, especially if it be new, you should say, "What is the cause? Why does it occur?" and you will in the course of time find out the reason.

Then, there is another point about these candles which will answer a question; that is, as to the way in which this fluid gets out of the cup, up the wick, and into the place of combustion. You know that the flames on these burning wicks in candles made of beeswax, stearin, or spermaceti, do not run down to the wax or other matter, and melt it all away, but keep to their own right place. They are fenced off from the fluid below, and do not encroach on the cup at the sides. I cannot imagine a more beautiful example than the condition of adjustment under which a candle makes one part subserve to the other to the very end of its action. A combustible thing like that, burning away gradually, never being intruded upon by the flame,

is a very beautiful sight; especially when you come to learn what a vigorous thing flame is—what power it has of destroying the wax itself when it gets hold of it, and of disturbing its proper form if it come only too near.

But how does the flame get hold of the fuel? There is a beautiful point about that—*capillary attraction*.[3] "Capillary attraction!" you say, "the attraction of hairs." Well, never mind the name: it was given in old times, before we had a good understanding of what the real power was. It is by what is called capillary attraction that the fuel is conveyed to the part where combustion goes on, and is deposited there, not in a careless way, but very beautifully in the very midst of the center of action which takes place around it. Now, I am going to give you one or two instances of capillary attraction. It is that kind of action or attraction which makes two things that do not dissolve in each other still hold together. When you wash your hands, you wet them thoroughly; you take a little soap to make the adhesion better, and you find your hand remains wet. This is by that kind of attraction of which I am about to speak. And, what is more, if your hands are not soiled (as they almost always are by the usages of life), if you put your finger into a little warm water, the water

will creep a little way up the finger, though you may not stop to examine it.

I have here a substance which is rather porous— a column of salt—and I will pour into the plate at the bottom, not water, as it appears, but a saturated solution of salt which cannot absorb more; so that the action which you will see will not be due to its dissolving anything. We may consider the plate to be the candle, and the salt the wick, and this solution the melted tallow. (I have colored the fluid, that you may see the action better.) You observe that, now I pour in the fluid, it rises and gradually creeps up the salt higher and higher; and provided the column does not tumble over, it will go to the top. If this dark solution were combustible, and we were to place a wick at the top of the salt, it would burn as it entered into the wick.

It is a most curious thing to see this kind of ac-

The fluid in the plate gradually creeps up the column of salt.

tion taking place, and to observe how singular some of the circumstances are about it. When you wash your hands, you take a towel to wipe off the water; and it is by that kind of wetting, or that kind of attraction which makes the towel become wet with water, that the wick is made wet with the tallow. I have known some careless boys and girls (indeed, I have known it happen to careful people as well) who, having washed their hands and wiped them with a towel, have thrown the towel over the side of the basin, and before long it has drawn all the water out of the basin and conveyed it to the floor, because it happened to be thrown over the side in such a way as to serve the purpose of a siphon.[4]

That you may the better see the way in which the substances act one upon another, I have here a vessel made of wire gauze filled with water, and

The damp towel serves as a siphon and draws the water out of the basin by capillary attraction.

you may compare it in its action to the cotton in one respect, or to a piece of calico in the other. In fact, wicks are sometimes made of a kind of wire gauze. You will observe that this vessel is a porous thing; for if I pour a little water onto the top, it will run out at the bottom. You would be puzzled for a good while if I asked you what the state of this vessel is, what is inside it, and why it is there? The vessel is full of water, and yet you see the water goes in and runs out as if it were empty. In order to prove this to you, I have only to empty it. The reason is this: the wire, being once wetted, remains wet; the meshes are so small that the fluid is attracted so strongly from the one side to the other, as to remain in the vessel although it is porous. In like manner the particles of melted tallow ascend the cotton and get to the top; other particles then follow by their mutual attraction for each other, and as they reach the flame they are gradually burned.

Here is another application of the same principle. You see this bit of rattan cane. I have seen boys about the streets, who are very anxious to appear like men, take a piece of cane, and light it and smoke it, as an imitation of a cigar. They are enabled to do so by the permeability of the cane in one direction, and by its capillarity. If I place this

piece of cane on a plate containing some camphine
(which is very much like paraffin in its general
character), exactly in the same manner as the
dark fluid rose through the salt will this fluid rise
through the piece of cane. There being no pores
at the side, the fluid cannot go in that direction,

*The camphine rises by
capillary attraction
through the inside of the
cane and can be
ignited at the top.*

but must pass through its length. Already the fluid
is at the top of the cane: now I can light it and
make it serve as a candle. The fluid has risen by
the capillary attraction of the piece of cane, just
as it does through the cotton in the candle.

Now, the only reason why the candle does not
burn all down the side of the wick is that the
melted tallow extinguishes the flame. You know
that a candle, if turned upside down, so as to allow
the fuel to run upon the wick, will be put out.
The reason is that the flame has not had time to
make the fuel hot enough to burn, as it does above,

where it is carried in small quantities into the wick, and has all the effect of the heat exercised upon it.

There is another condition which you must learn as regards the candle, without which you would not be able fully to understand the philosophy of it, and that is the vaporous condition of the fuel. In order that you may understand that, let me show you a very pretty, but very commonplace experiment. If you blow a candle out cleverly, you will see the vapor rise from it. You have, I know, often smelled the vapor of a blown-out candle— and a very bad smell it is; but if you blow it out cleverly, you will be able to see pretty well the vapor into which this solid matter is transformed. I will blow out one of these candles in such a way as not to disturb the air around it, by the continuing action of my breath; and now, if I hold a

When the small quantities of oil in the wick are heated by the flame, they turn into vapor. This vapor is combustible, while still hot, even after the flame is blown out.

lighted taper two or three inches from the wick, you will observe a train of fire going through the air till it reaches the candle. I am obliged to be quick and ready, because, if I allow the vapor time to cool, it becomes condensed into a liquid or solid, or the stream of combustible matter gets disturbed.

Now, as to the shape or form of the flame. It concerns us much to know about the condition which the matter of the candle finally assumes at the top of the wick—where you have such beauty and brightness as nothing but combusion or flame can produce. You have the glittering beauty of gold and silver, and the still higher luster of jewels, like the ruby and diamond; but none of these rival the brilliancy and beauty of flame. What diamond can shine like flame? It owes its luster at nighttime to the very flame shining upon it. The flame shines in darkness, but the light which the diamond has is as nothing until the flame shines upon it, when it is brilliant again. The candle alone shines by itself, and for itself, or for those who have arranged the materials.

Now, let us look a little at the form of the flame as you see it under the glass shade. It is steady and equal; and its general form is that which is represented in the diagram, varying with atmospheric

disturbances, and also varying according to the size of the candle. It is a bright oblong—brighter at the top than towards the bottom—with the wick in the middle, and besides the wick in the middle, certain darker parts towards the bottom, where the ignition is not so perfect as in the part above.

I have a drawing here, sketched many years ago by Hooker, when he made his investigations. It is the drawing of the flame of a lamp, but it will apply to the flame of a candle. The cup of the candle is the vessel or lamp, the melted spermaceti is the oil, and the wick is common to both. Upon that he sets this little flame, and then he represents what is true—a certain quantity of matter rising about it which you do not see, and which, if you have not been here before, or are not familiar with the subject, you will not know of. He has here represented the parts of the surrounding atmosphere that are very essential to the flame, and that are always present with it. There is a current formed, which draws the flame out—for the flame which you see is really drawn out by the current, and drawn upward to a great height—just as Hooker has here shown you by that prolongation of the current in the diagram. You may see this by taking a lighted candle, and putting it in the sun so as

to get its shadow thrown on a piece of paper. How remarkable it is that that thing which is light enough to produce shadows of other objects, can be made to throw its own shadow on a piece of white paper or card, so that you can actually see streaming round the flame something which is not part of the flame, but is ascending and drawing the flame upwards. Now, I am going to imitate the sunlight, by applying the voltaic battery to the electric lamp. You now see our sun, and its great luminosity; and by placing a candle between it and the screen, we get the shadow of the flame. You observe the shadow of the candle and of the wick; then there is a darkish part, as represented in the diagram, and then a part which is more distinct. Curiously enough, however, what we see in

The flame is brightest at the top and darker towards the bottom.

The column of hot air, seen in the shadow, draws the flame out and upward.

the shadow as the darkest part of the flame is, in reality, the brightest part; and here you see streaming upwards the ascending current of hot air, as shown by Hooker, which draws out the flame, supplies it with air, and cools the sides of the cup of melted fuel.

I can give you here a little further illustration, for the purpose of showing you how flame goes up or down, according to the current. I have here a flame—it is not a candle flame—but you can, no doubt, by this time, generalize enough to be able to compare one thing with another. What I am about to do is to change the ascending current that takes the flame upwards into a descending current. This I can easily do by the little apparatus you see before me. The flame, as I have said, is not a candle flame, but it is produced by alcohol, so that it shall not smoke too much. I will also color the flame with another substance,[5] so that you may trace its course; for with the spirit alone you could hardly see well enough to have the opportunity of tracing its direction. By lighting this spirit-of-wine, we have then produced a flame; and you observe that when held in the air, it naturally goes upwards. You understand now easily enough why flames go up under ordinary circumstances—it is because of the draft of air by which

When the flame is blown downwards, the direction of the current of air is changed to a descending current.

the combustion is formed. But now, by blowing the flame down, you see I am enabled to make it go downwards into this little chimney—the direction of the current being changed. Before we have concluded this course of lectures, we shall show you a lamp in which the flame goes up and the smoke goes down, or the flame goes down and the smoke goes up. You see, then, that we have the power in this way of varying the flame in different directions.

There are now some other points that I must bring before you. Many of the flames you see here vary very much in their shape by the currents of air blowing around them in different directions; but we can, if we like, make flames so that they will look like fixtures, and we can photograph them—indeed, we have to photograph them—so

that they become fixed to us, if we wish to find out everything concerning them. That, however, is not the only thing I wish to mention. If I take a flame sufficiently large, it does not keep that homogeneous, that uniform condition of shape, but it breaks out with a power of life which is quite wonderful. I am about to use another kind

A large ball of cotton immersed in spirit and lighted causes fine tongues of flame to rise up.

of fuel, but one which is truly and fairly a representative of the wax or tallow of a candle. I have here a large ball of cotton, which will serve as a wick. And, now that I have immersed it in spirit and applied a light to it, in what way does it differ from an ordinary candle? Why, it differs very much in one respect, that we have a vivacity and power about it, a beauty and a life entirely different from the light presented by a candle. You see those fine tongues of flame rising up. You have the same general disposition of the mass of the flame from below upwards; but, in addition to that, you have this remarkable breaking out into tongues which you do not perceive in the case of

a candle. Now, why is this? I must explain it to you, because when you understand that perfectly, you will be able to follow me better in what I have to say hereafter.

I suppose some here will have made for themselves the experiment I am going to show you. Am I right in supposing that anybody here has played at snapdragon? I do not know a more beautiful illustration of the philosophy of flame, as to a certain part of its history, than the game of snapdragon. First, here is the dish; and let me say, that when you play snapdragon properly, you ought to have the dish well warmed; you ought also to have warm raisins and warm brandy, which, however, I have not got. When you have put the brandy into the dish, you have the cup and the fuel; and are not the raisins acting like the wicks? I now throw the raisins into the dish, and light the spirit, and you see those beautiful tongues of flame that I refer to. You have the air creeping in over the edge of the dish forming these tongues. Why? Because, through the force of the current and the irregularity of the action of the flame, it cannot flow in one uniform stream. The air flows in so irregularly that you have what would otherwise be a single image, broken up into a variety of forms, and each of these little tongues has an inde-

pendent existence of its own. Indeed, I might say, you have here a multitude of independent candles.

You must not imagine, because you see these tongues all at once, that the flame is of this particular shape. A flame of that shape is never so at any one time. Never is a body of flame, like that which you just saw rising from the ball, of the shape it appears to you. It consists of a multitude of different shapes, succeeding each other so fast that the eye is only able to take cognizance of them all at once. They do not occur all at once: it is only because we see these shapes in such rapid succession that they seem to us to exist all at one time.

LECTURE II

A Candle: Brightness of the Flame

WE WERE occupied the last time we met in considering the general character and arrangement as regards the fluid portion of a candle, and the way in which that fluid got into the place of combustion. And now, I have to ask your attention to the means by which we are enabled to ascertain what happens in any particular part of the flame—why it happens, what it does in happening, and where, after all, the whole candle goes to: because, as you know very well, a candle being brought before us and burned, disappears, if burned properly, without the least trace of dirt in

the candlestick—and this is a very curious circumstance.

Here is a candle: I am about to put the end of this glass tube into the middle of the flame—into that part which is represented in the illustration as being rather dark, and which you can see at any time, if you will look at a candle carefully, without blowing it about. We will examine this dark part first.

Now I take this bent glass tube, and introduce one end into that part of the flame, and you see at once that something is coming from the flame, out at the other end of the tube; and if I put a flask there, and leave it for a little while, you will

When one end of a bent glass tube is placed in the middle of a candle flame, a heavy vaporous substance flows from the flame into the flask.

see that something from the middle part of the flame is gradually drawn out, and goes through the tube and into that flask, and there behaves very differently from what it does in the open air. It not only escapes from the end of the tube, but falls down to the bottom of the flask like a heavy substance, as indeed it is. We find that this is the wax of the candle made into a vaporous fluid—not a gas. (You must learn the difference between a gas and a vapor: a gas remains permanent, a vapor is something that will condense.) If you blow out a candle, you perceive a very nasty smell, resulting from the condensation of this vapor. That is very different from what you have outside the flame; and, in order to make that more clear to you, I am about to produce and set fire to a larger portion of this vapor—for what we have in the small way in a candle, to understand thoroughly, we must, as philosophers, produce in a larger way, if needful, that we may examine the different parts. And now I am about to show you what that vapor is. Here is some wax in a glass flask, and I am going to make it hot, over this lamp, as the inside of that candle flame is hot, and the matter about the wick is hot. You see that the wax I put in it has become fluid, and there is a little smoke coming from it. We shall very soon have the vapor rising

up. I will make it still hotter, and now we get more of it, so that I can actually pour the vapor out of the flask into that basin, and set it on fire there. This, then, is exactly the same kind of vapor as we have in the middle of the candle; and that you may be sure this is the case, let us try whether we have not got here, in this flask, a real combustible vapor out of the middle of the candle. See how it burns. Now, this is the vapor from the middle of the candle, produced by its own heat; and that is one of the first things you have to consider with respect to the progress of the wax in the course of its combustion, and as regards the changes it undergoes.

I will arrange another tube carefully in the flame, and I should not wonder if we were able, by a little care, to get that vapor to pass through the tube to the other extremity, where we will light it, and obtain absolutely the flame of the candle at a place distant from it. Now, look at that. Is not that a very pretty experiment? Talk about laying on gas—why, we can actually lay on a candle! And you see from this that there are clearly two different kinds of action—one the *production* of the vapor, and the other the *combustion* of it— both of which take place in particular parts of the candle.

*The vapor produced in the middle
of the flame can be carried through a
tube and ignited at the other end.*

I shall get no vapor from that part which is already burned. If I raise the tube to the upper part of the flame, as soon as the vapor has been swept out, what comes away will be no longer combustible: it is already burned. How burned? Why, burned thus: in the middle of the flame, where the wick is, there is this combustible vapor; on the outside of the flame is the air which we shall find necessary for the burning of the candle; between the two, intense chemical action takes place, whereby the air and the fuel act upon each other, and at the very same time that we obtain light the vapor inside is destroyed. If you examine where the heat of a candle is, you will find it very curiously arranged. Suppose I take this candle, and hold a piece of paper close upon the flame, where is the heat of that flame? Do you not see that it

If a piece of paper is held across the middle of a flame, a ring-shaped burn will appear, showing where the heat of the flame is.

is *not* in the inside? It is in a ring, exactly in the place where I told you the chemical action was; and even in my irregular mode of making the experiment, if there is not too much disturbance, there will always be a ring. This is a good experiment for you to make at home. Take a strip of paper, have the air in the room quiet, and put the piece of paper right across the middle of the flame and you will find that it is burned in two places, and that it is not burned, or very little so, in the middle; and when you have tried the experiment once or twice, so as to make it nicely, you will be very interested to see where the heat is, and to find that it is where the air and the fuel come together.

This is most important for us as we proceed with our subject. Air is absolutely necessary for com-

A jar is placed over a candle. The flame will fade and go out because it cannot burn without pure, fresh air.

bustion; and, what is more, I must have you understand that *fresh* air is necessary, or else we should be imperfect in our reasoning and our experiments. Here is a jar of air. I place it over a candle, and it burns very nicely in it at first, showing that what I have said about it is true; but there will soon be a change. See how the flame is drawing upwards, presently fading, and at last going out. And going out, why? Not because it wants air merely, for the jar is as full now as it was before; but it wants pure, fresh air. The jar is full of air, partly changed, partly not changed; but it does not contain sufficient of the fresh air which is necessary for the combustion of a candle. These are all points which we, as young chemists, have to gather up; and if we look a little more closely into this kind of action, we shall find certain steps

The Argand lamp (A) is connected to a flexible pipe (B) which permits air passage to the middle of the flame. The oil reservoir is at the left (C). If the air is shut off, the lamp will smoke because of imperfect combustion.

of reasoning extremely interesting. For instance, here is an oil lamp—an excellent lamp for our experiments—the old Argand lamp. I now make it like a candle; there is the cotton; there is the oil rising up it; and there is the conical flame. It burns poorly, because there is a partial restraint of air. I have allowed no air to get to it, save round the outside of the flame, and it does not burn well. I cannot admit more air from the outside, because the wick is large; but if, as Argand did so cleverly, I open a passage to the middle of the flame, and so let air come in there, you will see how much more beautifully it burns. If I shut the air off, look how it smokes; and why? We have now some very in-

teresting points to study. We have the case of the
combustion of a candle; we have the case of a can-
dle being put out by the want of air; and we have
now the case of imperfect combustion; and this is
to us so interesting, that I want you to understand
it as thoroughly as you do the case of a candle
burning in its best possible manner. I will now
make a great flame, because we need the largest
possible illustrations. Here is a larger wick. All
these things are the same as candles, after all. If we
have larger wicks, we must have a larger supply of
air, or we shall have less perfect combustion. Look
now at this black substance going up into the at-
mosphere; there is a regular stream of it. I have
provided means to carry off the imperfectly
burned part, lest it should annoy you. Look at the
soots that fly off from the flame: see what an im-
perfect combustion it is, because it cannot get
enough air. What, then, is happening? Why, cer-
tain things which are necessary to the combustion
of a candle are absent, and very bad results are ac-
cordingly produced; but we see what happens to a
candle when it is burned in a pure and proper state
of air. At the time when I showed you this char-
ring by the ring of flame on the one side of the
paper, I might have also shown you, by turning to
the other side, that the burning of a candle pro-

duces the same kind of soot—charcoal or carbon.

But, before I show that, let me explain to you—
as it is quite necessary for our purpose—that,
though I take a candle and give you, as the general
result, its combustion in the form of a flame, we
must see whether combustion is always in this con-
dition, or whether there are other conditions of
flame; and we shall soon discover that there are,
and that they are most important to us. Here is
a little gunpowder. You know that gunpowder
burns with flame—we may fairly call it flame.
It contains carbon and other materials, which al-
together cause it to burn with a flame. And here
is some pulverized iron, or iron filings. Now, I
propose burning these two things together. I have
a little mortar in which I will mix them. (Before
I go into these experiments, let me hope that none
of you, by trying to repeat them, for fun's sake,
will do any harm. These things may all be very
properly used if you take care; but without that,
much mischief will be done.) Well, then, here is
a little gunpowder, which I put at the bottom of
that little wooden vessel, and mix the iron fil-
ings up with it, my object being to make the gun-
powder set fire to the filings and burn them in
the air, and thereby show the difference between
substances burning with flame and not with flame.

Here is the mixture; and when I set fire to it, you must watch the combustion, and you will see that it is of two kinds. You will see the gunpowder burning with a flame, and the filings thrown up. You will see them burning too, but without the production of flame. They will each burn separately. There is the gunpowder, which burns with a flame; and there are the filings—they burn with a different kind of combustion. You see, then, these two great distinctions; and upon these differences depend all the utility and all the beauty of flame which we use for the purpose of giving out light. When we use oil, or gas, or candle for the purpose of illumination, their fitness all depends upon these different kinds of combustion.

There are such curious conditions of flame, that it requires some cleverness and nicety of discrimination to distinguish the kinds of combustion one from another. For instance, here is a powder which is very combustible, consisting, as you see, of separate little particles. It is called *lycopodium*,[6] and each of these particles can produce a vapor, and produce its own flame; but, to see them burning, you would imagine it was all one flame. I will now set fire to a quantity, and you will see the effect. We saw a cloud of flame, apparently in one body; but that rushing noise was a proof that the com-

bustion was not a continuous or regular one. This is the lightning of the pantomimes, and a very good imitation. This is not an example of combustion like that of the filings I have been speaking of, to which we must now return.

Suppose I take a candle, and examine that part of it which appears brightest to our eyes. Why, there I get these black particles, which already you have seen many times evolved from the flame, and which I am now about to evolve in a different way. I will take this candle and clear away the gutterage, which occurs by reason of the currents of air; and if I now arrange a glass tube so as just to dip into this luminous part, as in our first experiment, only higher, you see the result. In place of having the same white vapor that you had before, you will now have a black vapor. There it goes, as black as ink. It is certainly very different from the white vapor; and when we put a light to it, we shall find that it does not burn, but that it puts the light out. Well, these particles, as I said before, are just the smoke of the candle; and this brings to mind that old employment which Dean Swift recommended to servants for their amusement; namely, writing on the ceiling of a room with a candle. But what is that black substance? Why, it is the same carbon which exists in the

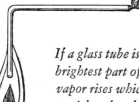

If a glass tube is placed in the brightest part of the flame, a black vapor rises which is made up of particles of carbon.

candle. How comes it out of the candle? It evidently existed in the candle, or else we should not have had it here. And now I want you to follow me in this explanation. You would hardly think that all those substances which fly about London, in the form of soots and blacks, are the very beauty and life of the flame, and which are burned in it as those iron filings were burned here. Here is a piece of wire gauze, which will not let the flame go through it; and I think you will see, almost immediately, that when I bring it low enough to touch that part of the flame which is otherwise so bright, that it quells and quenches it at once, and allows a volume of smoke to rise up.

I want you now to follow me in this point, that whenever a substance burns, as the iron filings burned in the flame of gunpowder, without assum-

ing the vaporous state (whether it becomes liquid or remains solid), it becomes exceedingly luminous. I have here taken three or four examples apart from the candle, on purpose to illustrate this point to you; because what I have to say is applicable to all substances, whether they burn or whether they do not burn: that they are exceedingly bright if they retain their solid state, and that it is to this presence of solid particles in the candle flame that it owes its brilliancy.

Here is a platinum wire, a body which does not change by heat. If I heat it in this flame, see how exceedingly luminous it becomes. I will make the flame dim, for the purpose of giving a little light only, and yet you will see that the heat which it can give to that platinum wire, though far less than the heat it has itself, is able to raise the platinum wire to a far higher state of effulgence. This flame has carbon in it; but I will take one that has no carbon in it. There is a material, a kind of fuel —a vapor, or gas, whichever you like to call it— in that vessel, and it has no solid particles in it; so I take that because it is an example of flame itself burning without any solid matter whatever; and if I now put this solid substance in it, you see what an intense heat it has, and how brightly it causes the solid body to glow. This is the pipe through

which we convey this particular gas, which we call hydrogen, and which you shall know all about next time we meet. And here is a substance called oxygen, by means of which this hydrogen can burn; and although we produce, by their mixture, far greater heat[7] than you can obtain from the candle, yet there is very little light. If, however, I take a solid substance, and put that into it, we produce an intense light. If I take a piece of lime, a substance which will not burn, and which will not vaporize by the heat (and because it does not vaporize, remains solid, and remains heated), you will soon observe what happens as to its glowing. I have here a most intense heat, produced by the burning of hydrogen in contact with the oxygen; but there is as yet very little light—not for want of heat, but for want of particles which can retain their solid state; but when I hold this piece of lime in the flame of the hydrogen as it burns in the oxygen, see how it glows! This is the glorious lime-light, which rivals the voltaic light, and which is almost equal to sunlight.

I have here a piece of carbon or charcoal, which will burn and give us light exactly in the same manner as if it were burned as part of a candle. The heat that is in the flame of a candle decomposes the vapor of the wax, and sets free the carbon

particles—they rise up heated and glowing as this now glows, and then enter into the air. But the particles when burned never pass off from a candle in the form of carbon. They go off into the air as a perfectly invisible substance, about which we shall know hereafter.

Is it not beautiful to think that such a process is going on, and that such a dirty thing as charcoal can become so incandescent? You see it comes to this: that all bright flames contain these solid particles, either during the time they are burning, as in the candle, or immediately after being burned, as in the case of the gunpowder and iron filings— all these things give us this glorious and beautiful light.

I will give you a few illustrations. Here is a piece of phosphorus, which burns with a bright flame. Very well; we may now conclude that phosphorus will produce, either at the moment that it is burning or afterwards, these solid particles. Here is the phosphorus lighted, and I cover it over with this glass for the purpose of keeping in what is produced. What is all that smoke? That smoke consists of those very particles which are produced by the combustion of the phosphorus. Here, again, are two substances. This is chlorate of potassa, and this other sulphuret of antimony. I shall mix

The smoke inside the glass cover consists of solid particles produced by the burning phosphorus.

these together a little, and then they may be burned in many ways. I shall touch them with a drop of sulphuric acid, for the purpose of giving you an illustration of chemical action, and they will instantly burn.[8] Now, from the appearance of things, you can judge for yourselves whether they produce solid matter in burning. I have given you the train of reasoning which will enable you to say whether they do or do not; for what is this bright flame but the solid particles pasing off?

There is in this furnace a very hot crucible— I am about to throw into it some zinc filings, and they will burn with a flame like gunpowder. I make this experiment because you can make it well at home. Now, I want you to see what will be the result of the combustion of this zinc. Here

it is burning—burning beautifully like a candle, I may say. But what is all that smoke, and what are those little clouds of wool which will come to you if you cannot come to them, and make themselves sensible to you in the form of the old philosophic wool, as it was called? We shall have left in that crucible, also, a quantity of this woolly matter. But I will take a piece of this same zinc and make an experiment a little more closely at home, as it were. You will have here the same thing happening. Here is the piece of zinc, there [pointing to a jet burning a flame of hydrogen] is the furnace, and we will set to work and try and burn the metal. It glows, you see: there is the combustion, and there is the white substance into which it burns. And so, if I take that flame of hydrogen as the representative of a candle, and show you a substance like zinc burning in the flame, you will see that it was merely during the action of combustion that this substance glowed— while it was kept hot; and if I take a flame of hydrogen, and put this white substance from the zinc into it, look how beautifully it glows, and just because it is a solid substance.

I will now take such a flame as I had a moment since, and set free from it the particles of carbon. Here is some camphine, which will burn with a

smoke; but if I send these particles of smoke through this pipe into the hydrogen flame, you will see they will burn and become luminous, because we heat them a second time. There they are. Those are the particles of carbon reignited a second time. They are those particles which you can easily see by holding a piece of paper behind them, and which, whilst they are in the flame, are ignited by the heat produced, and, when so ignited, produce this brightness. When the particles are not separated, you get no brightness. The flame of coal gas owes its brightness to the separation, during combustion, of these particles of carbon, which are equally in that as in a candle.

I can very quickly alter that arrangement. Here, for instance, is a bright flame of gas. Supposing I add so much air to the flame as to cause it all to burn before those particles are set free, I shall not have this brightness; and I can do that in this way: if I place over the jet this wire-gauze cap, as you see, and then light the gas over it, it burns with a nonluminous flame, owing to its having plenty of air mixed with it before it burns; and if I raise the gauze, you see it does not burn below.[9] There is plenty of carbon in the gas; but, because the atmosphere can get to it, and mix with it before it burns, you see how pale and blue the flame is. And

if I blow upon a bright gas flame, so as to consume all this carbon before it gets heated to the glowing point, it will also burn blue. The only reason why I have not the same bright light when I thus blow upon the flame is that the carbon meets with sufficient air to burn it before it gets separated in the flame in a free state. The difference is solely due to the solid particles not being separated before the gas is burned.

You observe that there are certain products as the result of the combustion of a candle, and that of these products one portion may be considered as charcoal, or soot; that charcoal, when afterwards burned, produces some other product; and it concerns us very much now to ascertain what that other product is. We showed that something was going away; and I want you now to understand how much is going up into the air; and for that purpose we will have combustion on a little larger scale. From that candle ascends heated air, and two or three experiments will show you the ascending current; but, in order to give you a notion of the quantity of matter which ascends in this way, I will make an experiment by which I shall try to imprison some of the products of this combustion. For this purpose I have here what boys call a fire balloon. I use this fire balloon merely as

a sort of measure of the result of the combustion we are considering; and I am about to make a flame in such an easy and simple manner as shall best serve my present purpose. This plate shall be the cup, we will so say, of the candle; this spirit shall be our fuel; and I am about to place this chimney over it, because it is better for me to do so than to let things proceed at random. I shall now light the fuel, and here at the top we shall get the results of the combustion. What we get at the top of that tube is exactly the same, generally speaking, as you

A fire balloon is placed over the chimney so that the results of the combustion of the fuel in the plate can be measured.

get from the combustion of a candle; but we do not get a luminous flame here, because we use a substance which is feeble in carbon.

I am about to put this balloon, not into action—because that is not my object—but to show you the effect which results from the action of those products which arise from the candle, as they arise here from the furnace. [The balloon was held over the chimney, when it immediately commenced to fill.] You see how it is disposed to ascend; but we must not let it up, because it might come in contact with those upper gaslights, and that would be very inconvenient. [The upper gaslights were turned out, and the balloon was allowed to ascend.]

Does not that show you what a large bulk of matter is being evolved? Now, there is going through this tube [placing a large glass tube over a candle] all the products of that candle, and you will presently see that the tube will become quite opaque. Suppose I take another candle, and place it under a jar, and then put a light on the other side, just to show you what is going on. You see that the sides of the jar become cloudy, and the light begins to burn feebly. It is the products, you see, which make the light so dim, and this is the same thing which makes the sides of the jar so

opaque. If you go home and take a spoon that has been in the cold air, and hold it over a candle—not so as to soot it—you will find that it becomes dim, just as that jar is dim. And now, just to carry your thoughts forward to the time we shall next meet, let me tell you that it is *water* which causes the dimness; and when we next meet, I will show you that we can make it, without difficulty, assume the form of a liquid.

Products: Water from the Combustion

I DARE say you will remember that in the last lecture we had just mentioned the "products" from the candle. For when a candle burns we found we were able, by nice adjustment, to get various products from it. There was one substance which was not obtained when the candle was burning properly, which was charcoal or smoke; and there was some other substance that went upwards from the flame which did not appear as smoke, but took some other form, and made part of that general current which, ascending from the candle upwards, becomes invisible,

and escapes. There were also other products to mention. You remember that in that rising current having its origin at the candle, we found that one part was condensable against a cold spoon, or against a clean plate, or any other cold thing, and another part was incondensable.

We will first take the condensable part, and examine it; and, strange to say, we find that that part of the product is just water—nothing but water. On the last occasion I spoke of it incidentally, merely saying that water was produced among the condensable products of the candle; but today I wish to draw your attention to water, that we may examine it carefully, especially in relation to this subject, and also with respect to its general existence on the surface of the globe.

Now, having previously arranged an experiment for the purpose of condensing water from the products of the candle, my next point will be to show you this water; and perhaps one of the best means that I can adopt for showing its presence to so many at once, is to exhibit a very visible action of water, and then to apply that test to what is collected as a drop at the bottom of that vessel. I have here a chemical substance, discovered by Sir Humphry Davy, which has a very energetic action upon water. If I take a little

piece of it—it is called potassium, as coming from potash—if I take a little piece of it, and throw it into that basin, you see how it shows the presence of water by lighting up and floating about, burning with a violent flame. If I take away the candle which has been burning beneath this vessel containing ice and salt, you will see a drop of water—a condensed product of the candle—hanging from under the surface of the dish. I will

Vapor produced by the combustion of the candle condenses on the surface of a cold vessel and a drop of water is formed.

show you that potassium has the same action upon it as upon the water in that basin in the experiment we have just tried. It takes fire, and burns in just the same manner. I will take another drop upon this glass slab, and when I put the potassium on to it, you see at once, from its taking fire, that there is water present. Now, that water was produced by the candle. In the same manner, if I put this spirit lamp under that jar, you will soon see

the latter become damp, from the dew which is deposited upon it—that dew being the result of combustion; and I have no doubt you will shortly see by the drops of water which fall upon the paper below, that there is a good deal of water produced from the combustion of the lamp.

So, if I take a gas lamp, and put any cooling arrangement over it, I shall get water—water being likewise produced from the combustion of gas. Here, in this bottle, is a quantity of water—perfectly pure, distilled water, produced from the combustion of a gas lamp—in no point different from the water that you distill from the river, or ocean, or spring, but exactly the same thing. Water is one individual thing—it never changes. We can add to it by careful adjustment, for a little while, or we can take it apart, and get other things from it; but water, as water, remains always the same, either in a solid, liquid, or fluid state. Here, again, is some water produced by the combustion of an oil lamp. A pint of oil, when burned fairly and properly, produces rather more than a pint of water. And so we can go on with almost all combustible substances, and find that if they burn with a flame, as a candle, they produce water. You may make these experiments yourselves. The head of a poker is a very good thing to try with,

and if it remains cold long enough over the candle, you may get water condensed in drops on it; or a spoon or ladle, or anything else may be used, provided it be clean, and can carry off the heat, and so condense the water.

And now—to go into the history of this wonderful production of water from combustibles, and by combustion—I must first of all tell you that this water may exist in different conditions; and although you may now be acquainted with all its forms, they still require us to give a little attention to them for the present, so that we may perceive how the water, whilst it goes through its protean changes, is entirely and absolutely the same thing, whether it is produced from a candle, by combustion, or from the rivers or ocean.

First of all, water, when at the coldest, is ice. Now, we philosophers speak of water as water, whether it be in its solid, or liquid, or gaseous state —we speak of it chemically as water. Water is a thing compounded of two substances, one of which we have derived from the candle, and the other we shall find elsewhere. Water may occur as ice. Ice changes back into water when the temperature is raised: water also changes into steam when it is warmed enough. The water which we have here before us is in its densest state,[10] and

although it changes in weight, in condition, in form, and in many other qualities, it still is water; and whether we alter it into ice by cooling, or whether we change it into steam by heat, it increases in volume—in the one case very strangely and powerfully, and in the other case very largely and wonderfully.

Let us take the case of water changing into ice: we can effect that by cooling it in a mixture of salt and pounded ice;[11] and I shall do so to show you

A cast-iron bottle filled with water is placed in a freezing mixture. When the water freezes, the expansion is so great that it causes the bottle to crack open.

the expansion of water into a thing of larger bulk when it is so changed. The bottles we shall use are made of strong cast iron, very strong and very thick—I suppose they are the third of an inch in thickness; they are very carefully filled with water, so as to exclude all air, and then they are screwed down tight. We shall see that when we freeze the water in these iron vessels, they will not be able to hold the ice, and the expansion within them will break them in pieces. I am about to put

these two bottles into that mixture of ice and salt, for the purpose of showing that when water becomes ice, it changes in volume in this extraordinary way.

I have put our iron bottles containing water into this freezing mixture, that you may see what happens. No communication will take place, you observe, between the water in the bottles and the ice in the outer vessel. But there will be a conveyance of heat from the one to the other; and if we are successful you will by and by, so soon as the cold has taken possession of the bottles and their contents, hear a pop on the occasion of the bursting of the one bottle or the other; and, when we come to examine the bottles, we shall find their contents masses of ice, partly enclosed by the covering of iron which is too small for them, because the ice is larger in bulk than the water. You know very well that ice floats upon water: if a boy falls through a hole into the water, he tries to get on the ice again to float him up. Why does the ice float? Think of that, and philosophize. Because the ice is larger than the quantity of water which can produce it; and therefore the ice weighs the lighter, and the water is the heavier.

Ah! There is one of our bottles burst, and there is a crack down one side an eighth of an inch in

width. This other bottle is also broken; although the iron was nearly half an inch thick, the ice has burst it asunder. These changes always take place in water: they do not require to be always produced by artificial means—we only use them here because we want to produce a small winter round that little bottle, instead of a long and severe one. But if you go to Canada, or to the North, you will find the temperature there out of doors will do the same thing as has been done here by the freezing mixture.

I will pour some water into this tin cylinder; and, seeing how much water I pour in, you may easily estimate for yourselves how high it will rise in the vessel: it will cover the bottom about two inches. I am now about to convert the water into steam, for the purpose of showing to you the different volumes which water occupies in its different states of water and steam.

Look at the change which has taken place in the water to which we have applied heat—it is losing its fluid state. You may tell this by two or three circumstances. I have covered the mouth of this glass flask, in which water is boiling, with a watch glass. Do you see what happens? It rattles away like a valve chattering, because the steam rising from the boiling water sends the valve

up and down, and forces itself out, and so makes it clatter. You can very easily perceive that the flask is quite full of steam, or else it would not force its way out. You see, also, that the flask contains a substance very much larger than the water, for it fills the whole of the flask over and over again, and there it is blowing away into the air; and yet you cannot observe any great diminution in the bulk of the water, which shows you that its change of bulk is very great when it becomes steam.

What a stream of vapor is issuing from this tin vessel! You observe, we must have made it quite full of steam to have it sent out in that great quantity. And now, as we can convert the water into steam by heat, we convert it back into liquid water by the application of cold. And if we take a glass, or any other cold thing, and hold it over this steam, see how soon it gets damp with water; it will condense it until the glass is warm—it condenses the water which is now running down the sides of it. I have here another experiment to show the condensation of water from a vaporous state back into a liquid state, in the same way as the vapor, one of the products of the candle, was condensed against the bottom of the dish, and obtained in the form of water; and to show you how

Heat converts the water in the flask into steam.

The flask is closed at the top. If cold water is poured on the outside, the steam inside turns to water and the vessel collapses.

truly and thoroughly these changes take place, I will take this tin flask, which is now full of steam, and close the top. We shall see what takes place when we cause this water or steam to return back to the fluid state by pouring some cold water on the outside. [With the water, the vessel immediately collapsed.] You see what has happened. If I had closed the stopper, and still kept the heat applied to it, it would have burst the vessel; yet, when the steam returns to the state of water, the vessel collapses, there being a vacuum produced inside by the condensation of the steam. I show you these experiments for the purpose of pointing out that in all these occurrences there is nothing that changes the water into any other thing—it

still remains water; and so the vessel is obliged to give way, and is crushed inwards, as in the other case, by the further application of heat, it would have been blown outwards.

And what do you think the bulk of that water is when it assumes the vaporous condition? You see that cube [pointing to a cubic foot]. There, by its side, is a cubic inch, exactly the same shape as

One cubic inch of water is sufficient to expand into one cubic foot of steam.

the cubic foot, and that bulk of water [the cubic inch] is sufficient to expand into that bulk of steam [the cubic foot]; and, on the contrary, the application of cold will contract that large quantity of steam into this small quantity of water.

To return to our quiet philosophy. We shall not in future be deceived, therefore, by any changes that are produced in water. Water is the same everywhere, whether produced from the ocean or from the flame of the candle. Where, then, is this water which we get from a candle?

I must anticipate a little, and tell you. It evidently comes, as to part of it, from the candle; but is it within the candle beforehand? No. It is not in the candle; and it is not in the air round about the candle which is necessary for its combustion. It is neither in one nor the other, but it comes from their conjoint action, a part from the candle, a part from the air; and this we have now to trace, so that we may understand thoroughly what is the chemical history of a candle when we have it burning on our table. How shall we get at this? I myself know plenty of ways, but I want *you* to get at it from the association in your own minds of what I have already told you.

I think you can see a little in this way. We had just now the case of a substance which acted upon the water in the way that Sir Humphry Davy showed us,[12] and which I am now going to recall to your minds by making again an experiment upon that dish. It is a thing which we have to handle very carefully, for you see, if I allow a little splash of water to come upon this mass, it sets fire to part of it; and if there were free access of air, it would quickly set fire to the whole. Now, this is a metal—a beautiful and bright metal—which rapidly changes in the air, and, as you know, rapidly changes in water. I will put a piece on the

water, and you see it burns beautifully, making
a floating lamp, using the water in the place of air.

Again, if we take a few iron filings and put
them in water, we find that they likewise undergo
an alteration. They do not change so much as
this potassium does, but they change somewhat
in the same way; they become rusty, and show
an action upon the water, though in a different
degree of intensity to what this beautiful metal
does: but they act upon the water in the same
manner generally as this potassium. I want you
to put these different facts together in your
minds. I have another metal here, and when we
examined it with regard to the solid substance
produced by its combustion, we had an opportu-
nity of seeing that it burned; and I suppose, if I
take a little strip of this zinc and put it over the
candle, you will see something halfway, as it were,
between the combustion of potassium on the water
and the action of iron—you see there is a sort of
combustion. It has burned, leaving a white ash
or residuum, and here also we find that the metal
has a certain amount of action upon water.

By degrees we have learned how to modify the
action of these different substances, and to make
them tell us what we want to know. And now,
first of all, I take iron. It is a common thing in all

chemical reactions, where we get any result of this kind, to find that it is increased by the action of heat; and if we want to examine minutely and carefully the action of bodies one upon another, we often have to refer to the action of heat. You are aware, I believe, that iron filings burn beautifully in the air; but I am about to show you an experiment of this kind, because it will impress upon you what I am going to say about iron in its action on water. If I take a flame and make it hollow—you know why, because I want to get air to it and into it, and therefore I make it hollow— and then take a few iron filings and drop them into the flame, you see how well they burn. That combustion results from the chemical action which is going on when we ignite those particles. And so we proceed to consider these different effects, and ascertain what iron will do when it meets with water. It will tell us the story so beautifully, so gradually and regularly, that I think it will please you very much.

I have here a furnace with a pipe going through it like an iron gun barrel, and I have stuffed that barrel full of bright iron turnings, and placed it across the fire, to be made red-hot. We can either send air through the barrel to come in contact with the iron, or we can send steam from this

The flow of steam from the boiler is controlled by a stopcock. The pipe filled with iron turnings goes through a furnace and becomes red hot. The gas formed in the pipe passes into jars containing colored water.

little boiler at the end of the barrel. Here is a stopcock which shuts off the steam from the barrel until we wish to admit it. There is some water in these glass jars, which I have colored blue, so that you may see what happens. Now, you know very well that any steam I might send through that barrel, if it went through into the water, would be condensed; for you have seen that steam cannot retain its gaseous form if it be cooled down. You saw it here crushing itself into a small bulk, and causing the flask holding it to collapse; so that if I were to send steam through the barrel, it would be condensed—supposing the barrel were cold: it is, therefore, heated to perform the experiment I am now about to show you. I am going to send the steam through the barrel in small quantities; and you shall judge for yourselves, when you see it

issue from the other end, whether it still remains steam.

Steam is condensable into water, and when you lower the temperature of steam, you convert it back into fluid water; but I have lowered the temperature of the gas which I have collected in this jar, by passing it through water after it has traversed the iron barrel, and still it does not change back into water. I will take another test and apply it to this gas. (I hold the jar in an inverted position, or my substance would escape.) If I now apply a light to the mouth of the jar, it ignites with a slight noise. That tells you that it is not steam. Steam puts out a fire—it does not burn; but you saw that what I had in that jar burned.

We may obtain this substance equally from water produced from the candle flame as from any other source. When it is obtained by action of the iron upon the aqueous vapor, it leaves the iron in a state very similar to that in which these filings were after they were burned. It makes the iron heavier than it was before. So long as the iron remains in the tube and is heated, and is cooled again without the access of air or water, it does not change in its weight; but after having had this current of steam passed over it, it then comes out heavier than it was before, having taken some-

thing out of the steam, and having allowed something else to pass forth, which we see here.

Now, as we have another jar full, I will show you something most interesting. It is a combustible gas; I might at once take this jar and set fire to the contents, and show you that it is combustible; but I intend to show you more if I can. It is also a very light substance. Steam will condense: this body will rise in the air, and not condense. Suppose I take another glass jar, empty of all but air: if I examine it with a taper, I shall find that it contains nothing but air. I will now take this jar full of the gas that I am speaking of, and deal with it as though it were a light body. I will hold both upside down, and turn the one up under the other; and that which did contain the gas procured from the steam, what does it contain now? You will find it now contains only air. But look! Here is the combustible substance which I have poured out of the one jar into the other. It still preserves its quality, and condition, and independence, and therefore is the more worthy of our consideration, as belonging to the products of a candle.

Now, this substance which we have just prepared by the action of iron on the steam or water, we can also get by means of those other things which you have already seen act so well upon the

water. If I take a piece of potassium, and make the necessary arrangements, it will produce this gas; and if, instead, a piece of zinc, I find, when I come to examine it very carefully, that the main reason why this zinc cannot act upon the water continuously as the other metal does, is because the result of the action of the water envelops the zinc in a kind of protecting coat. We have learned in consequence, that if we put into our vessel only the zinc and water, they by themselves do not give rise to much action, and we get no result. But suppose I proceed to dissolve off this varnish— this encumbering substance—which I can do by a little acid; the moment I do this, I find the zinc acting upon the water exactly as the iron did, but at the common temperature. The acid in no way is altered, except in its combination with the oxide of zinc, which is produced. I have now

Acid added to a piece of zinc in a jar of water will produce hydrogen. The hydrogen is combustible.

poured the acid into the glass, and the effect is as though I were applying heat to cause this boiling up. There is something coming off from the zinc very abundantly, which is not steam. There is a jar full of it; and you will find that I have exactly the same combustible substance remaining in the vessel, when I hold it upside down, that I produced during the experiment with the iron barrel. This is what we get from water—the same substance which is contained in the candle.

Let us now trace distinctly the connection between these two points. This is hydrogen—a body classed among those things which in chemistry we call elements, because we can get nothing else out of them. A candle is not an elementary body, because we can get carbon out of it; we can get this hydrogen out of it, or at least out of the water which it supplies. And this gas has been so named hydrogen, because it is that element which, in association with another, generates water.* Here are two or three jars with which we shall make a few experiments, and I want to show you the best way of making these experiments. I am not afraid to show you, for I wish you to make experiments, if you will only make them with care and attention,

* Ὕδωρ, "water," and γεννάω, "I generate."

and the assent of those around you. As we advance in chemistry, we are obliged to deal with substances which are rather injurious, if in their wrong places—the acids, and heat, and combustible things we use, might do harm if carelessly employed.

If you want to make hydrogen, you can make it easily from bits of zinc, and sulphuric or muriatic acid. Here is what in former times was called the "philosopher's candle." It is a little vial with a cork, and a tube or pipe passing through it. And I am now putting a few little pieces of zinc into it. This little instrument I am going to apply to a useful purpose in our demonstrations—for I want to show you that you can prepare hydrogen, and make some experiments with it as you please at your own homes. Let me here tell you why I am so careful to fill this vial nearly, and yet not quite full. I do it because the evolved gas, which, as

The "philosopher's candle." Hydrogen formed by the action of zinc and sulphuric acid in water passes through the tube in the cork. If a light is applied to the top of the tube, the hydrogen will burn.

you have seen, is very combustible, is explosive to a considerable extent when mixed with air, and might lead to harm, if you were to apply a light to the end of that pipe before all the air had been swept out of the space above the water. I am now about to pour in the sulphuric acid. I have used very little zinc, and more sulphuric acid and water, because I want to keep it at work for some time. I therefore take care in this way to modify the proportions of the ingredients, so that I may have a regular supply—not too quick, and not too slow.

Suppose I now take a glass and put it upside down over the end of the tube, because the hydrogen is light I expect that it will remain in that vessel a little while. We will now test the contents of our glass to see if there be hydrogen in it. I think I am safe in saying we have caught some. There it is, you see. I will now apply a light to the top of the tube. There is the hydrogen burning. There is our philosophical candle. It is a foolish, feeble sort of a flame, you may say; but it is so hot that scarcely any common flame gives out so much heat. It goes on burning regularly, and I am now about to put that flame to burn under a certain arrangement, in order that we may examine its results and make use of the information which we may thereby acquire.

Inasmuch as the candle produces water, and this gas comes out of the water, let us see what this gives us by the same process of combustion that the candle went through when it burnt in the atmosphere; and for that purpose I am going to put the lamp under this apparatus, in order to condense whatever may arise from the combustion within it. In the course of a short time

The vapor rising from the combustion of the hydrogen flame condenses in the cylinder placed over the "philosopher's candle" and turns into water.

you will see moisture appearing in the cylinder, and you will get the water running down the side; and the water from this hydrogen flame will have absolutely the same effect upon all our tests, being obtained by the same general process as in the former case. This hydrogen is a very beautiful substance. It is so light that it carries things up: it is far lighter than the atmosphere; and I dare say I can show you this by an experiment which, if you

are very clever, some of you may even have skill enough to repeat.

Here is our generator of hydrogen, and here are some soapsuds. I have an India-rubber tube connected with the hydrogen generator, and at the end of the tube is a tobacco pipe. I can thus put the pipe into the suds, and blow bubbles by means of the hydrogen. You observe how the bubbles fall downwards when I blow them with my warm breath; but notice the difference when I blow them with hydrogen. It shows you how light this gas must be in order to carry with it not merely the ordinary soap bubble, but the larger portion of a drop hanging to the bottom of it. I can show its lightness in a better way than this; larger bubbles than these may be so lifted up; indeed, in former times balloons used to be filled with this gas. We shall fasten this tube on to our generator, and we shall have a stream of hydrogen here with which we can charge this balloon made

The generator of hydrogen is blowing soap bubbles through an India-rubber tube connected to a tobacco pipe which has been placed in a vessel containing suds.

of collodion. I need not even be very careful to get all the air out, for I know the power of this gas to carry it up. Here is another larger one made of thin membrane, which we will fill and allow to ascend along with the smaller one. You will see they will all remain floating about until the gas escapes.

What, then, are the comparative weights of these substances? I have a table here which will show you the proportion which their weights bear to each other. I have taken a pint and a cubic foot as the measures, and have placed opposite to them the respective figures. A pint measure of this hydrogen weighs three quarters of our smallest weight (a grain), and a cubic foot weighs one twelfth of an ounce; whereas a pint of water weighs 8,750 grains, and a cubic foot of water weighs almost 1,000 ounces. You see, therefore, what a vast difference there is between the weight of a cubic foot of water and a cubic foot of hydrogen.

	HYDROGEN	WATER
1 pint	3/4 grain	8750 grains
1 cu. ft.	1/12 ounce	1000 ounces

Hydrogen gives rise to no substance that can become solid, either during combustion or afterwards as a product of its combustion. But when it burns, it produces water only; and if we take a cold glass and put it over the flame, it becomes damp, and you have water produced immediately in appreciable quantity; and nothing is produced by its combustion but the same water which you have seen the flame of the candle produce. It is important to remember that this hydrogen is the only thing in nature which furnishes water as the sole product of combustion.

And now we must endeavor to find some additional proof of the general character and composition of water. We have the power of arranging the zinc which you have seen acting upon the water by the assistance of an acid, in such a manner as to cause all the power to be evolved in the place where we require it. I have behind me a voltaic pile [a battery], and I am just about to show you its character and power. I hold here the extremities of the wires which transport the power from behind me, and which I shall cause to act on the water.

We have previously seen what a power of combustion is possessed by the potassium, or the zinc, or the iron filings; but none of them show such

A voltaic pile (or battery).
When contact is made between
the two wires, power of great
force and intensity is produced.

energy as this. [The Lecturer here made contact
between the two wires, when a brilliant flash of
light was produced.] This light is, in fact, pro-
duced by a forty-zinc power of burning: it is a
power that I can carry about in my hands, through
these wires, at pleasure—although, if I applied it
wrongly to myself, it would destroy me in an
instant, for it is a most intense thing, and the
power you see here put forth while you count five
is equivalent to the power of several thunder-
storms, so great is its force.[13] And that you may
see what intense energy it has, I will take the ends
of the wires which convey the power from the
battery, and with it I dare say I can burn this iron
file. Now, this is a chemical power, and one which,
in the next lecture, I shall apply to water, and
show you what results we are able to produce.

LECTURE **IV**

Hydrogen in the Candle

I SEE you are not tired of the candle yet, or I am sure you would not be interested in the subject in the way you are. When our candle was burning, we found it produced water exactly like the water we have around us; and by further examination of this water we found in it that curious body, hydrogen—that light substance of which there is some in this jar. We afterwards saw the burning powers of that hydrogen, and that it produced water. And I think I introduced to your notice an apparatus which I very briefly said was an arrangement of chemical force, or power, or energy, so

adjusted as to convey its power to us in these wires; and I said I should use that force to pull the water to pieces, to see what else there was in the water besides hydrogen; because, you remember, when we passed the water through the iron tube, we by no means got the weight of water back which we put in, in the form of steam, though we had a very large quantity of gas evolved. We have now to see what is the other substance present. That you may understand the character and use of this instrument, let us make an experiment or two.

Let us put together, first of all, some substances, knowing what they are, and then see what that instrument does to them. There is some copper (observe the various changes which it can undergo), and here is some nitric acid, and you will find that this, being a strong chemical agent, will act very powerfully when I add it to the copper. It is now sending forth a beautiful red vapor. The copper which I have put into the flask will dissolve: it will change the acid and the water into a blue fluid, containing copper and other things; and I propose then showing you how this voltaic battery deals with it; and in the meantime we will arrange another kind of experiment for you to see what power it has. This is a substance which is to us like water—that is to say, it contains bodies

which we do not know of as yet, as water contains a body which we do not know as yet. Now, this solution of a salt[14] I will put upon paper, and spread about, and apply the power of the battery to it, and observe what will happen. Three or four important things will happen which we shall take advantage of. I place this wetted paper upon a sheet of tinfoil, which is convenient for keeping all clean, and also for the advantageous application of the power; and this solution, you see, is not at all affected by being put upon the paper or tinfoil, nor by anything else I have brought in contact with it yet, and which, therefore, is free to us to use as regards that instrument. But first let us see that our instrument is in order. Here are our wires. Let us see whether it is in the state in which it was last time. We can soon tell. As yet, when I bring them together, we have no power, because the conveyers—what we call the electrodes—the passages or ways for the electricity—are stopped; but now this sudden flash at the ends of the wires has given me a telegram to say that it is ready. Before I begin our experiment I will get someone to break contact again at the battery behind me, and we will put a platinum wire across to connect the poles, and then if I find I can ignite a pretty good length of this wire, we shall be safe in our experi-

ment. Now you will see the power. [With the connection made, the wire became red hot.] There is the power running beautifully through the wire, which I have made thin on purpose to show you that we have those powerful forces; and now, having that power, we will proceed with it to the examination of water.

I have here two pieces of platinum, and if I lay them down upon this piece of paper [the moistened paper that was on the tinfoil], you will see no action; and if I take them up, there is no change that you can see, but the arrangement remains just as it was before. But, now, see what happens: if I take these two poles and put either one or the other of them down separately on the platinum plates, they do nothing for me, both are perfectly without action; but if I let them both be in con-

A piece of paper, wetted with a solution of acetate of lead, is placed on a sheet of tin foil. Two pieces of

platinum are on the ends of the battery. When both are placed on the paper, the positive pole will yield a brown mark.

tact at the same moment, see what happens. Look here at the effect that takes place, and see how I have pulled something apart from the white— something brown; and I have no doubt, if I were to arrange it thus, and were to put one of the poles to the tinfoil on the other side of the paper— why, I get such a beautiful action upon the paper, that I am going to see whether I cannot write with it—a telegram, if you please. See there how beautifully we can get our results!

You see we have here drawn something, which we have not known about before, out of this solution. Let us now take the other flask and see what we can draw out of that. This, you know, is a liquid which we have just made up from copper and nitric acid, whilst our other experiments were in hand; and though I am making this experiment very hastily, and may bungle a little, yet I prefer to let you see what I do rather than prepare it beforehand.

Now, see what happens. These two platinum plates are the two ends (or I will make them so immediately) of this apparatus; and I am about to put them in contact with that solution just as we did a moment ago on the paper. It does not matter to us whether the solution be on the paper or whether it be in the jar, so long as we bring the

ends of the apparatus to it. If I put the two platinums in by themselves, they come out as clean and as white as they go in; but when we take the power and lay that on, this, you see, is at once turned into copper, as it were: it has become like a plate of copper; and that has come out quite clean. If I take this coppered piece and change sides, the copper will leave the right-hand side and come over to the left side; what was before the coppered plate comes out clean, and the plate which was clean comes out coated with copper; and thus you see that the same copper we put into this solution we can also take out of it by means of this instrument.

Two platinum plates connected to a battery are placed in a flask which contains a solution of copper and nitric acid. The left plate becomes coppered.

Putting that solution aside, let us now see what effect this instrument will have upon water. Here are two little platinum plates which I intend to make the ends of the battery, and this [C] is a little vessel so shaped as to enable me to take it to

pieces, and show you its construction. In these two cups [A and B] I pour mercury, which touches the ends of the wires connected with the platinum plates. In the vessel [C] I pour some water containing a little acid (but which is put only for the purpose of facilitating the action; it undergoes no change in the process), and connected with the top of the vessel is a bent glass tube [D], which may remind you of the pipe which was connected with the gun barrel in our furnace experiment, and which now passes under the jar [F]. I have now adjusted this apparatus, and we will proceed to affect the water in some way or other. In the other case, I sent the water through a tube which was made red-hot; I am now going to pass the electricity through the contents of this vessel. Perhaps I may boil the water; if I do boil the water, I shall get steam; and you know

The decomposition of water by means of electricity. Gas is collected in jar F by the action of the battery on the water.

that steam condenses when it gets cold, and you will therefore see by that whether I do boil the water or not. Perhaps, however, I shall not boil the water, but produce some other effect. You shall have the experiment and see. There is one wire which I will put to this side [A], and here is the other wire which I will put to the other side [B], and you will soon see whether any disturbance takes place. Here it is seeming to boil up famously; but does it boil? Let us see whether that which goes out is steam or not. I think you will soon see the jar [F] will be filled with vapor, if that which rises from the water is steam. But can it be steam? Why, certainly not; because there it remains, you see, unchanged. There it is standing over the water, and it cannot therefore be steam, but must be a permanent gas of some sort. What is it? Is it hydrogen? Is it anything else? Well, we will examine it. If it is hydrogen, it will burn. It is certainly something combustible, but not combustible in the way that hydrogen is. Hydrogen would not have given you that noise; but the color of that light, when the thing did burn, was like that of hydrogen: it will, however, burn without contact with the air. That is why I have chosen this other form of apparatus, for the purpose of pointing out to you what are the particular circumstances of

A closed vessel (G) contains the gas which has been collected from jar F. An electric spark from the Leyden jar (L) explodes the gas and produces water.

this experiment. In place of an open vessel I have taken one that is closed (our battery is so beautifully active that we are even boiling the mercury, and getting all things right—not wrong, but vigorously right); and I am going to show you that that gas, whatever it may be, can burn without air, and in that respect differs from a candle, which cannot burn without the air. And our manner of doing this is as follows: I have here a glass vessel [G] which is fitted with two platinum wires [I, K], through which I can apply electricity; and we can put the vessel on the air pump and exhaust the air, and when we have taken the air out we can bring it here and fasten it on to this jar [F], and let into the vessel that gas which was formed by the action of the voltaic battery upon the water, and which we have produced by changing the water into it—for I may go as far as

this, and say we have really, by that experiment, changed the water into that gas. We have not only altered its condition, but we have changed it really and truly into that gaseous substance, and all the water is there which was decomposed by the experiment. As I screw this vessel [G, H] on here [H], and make the tubes well connected, and when I open the stopcocks [H, H, H], if you watch the level of the water [in F], you will see that the gas will rise. I will now close the stopcocks, as I have drawn up as much as the vessel can hold, and being safely conveyed into that chamber, I will pass into it an electric spark from this Leyden jar [L], when the vessel, which is now quite clear and bright, will become dim. There will be no sound, for the vessel is strong enough to confine the explosion. Did you see that brilliant light? If I again screw the vessel on to the jar, and open these stopcocks, you will see that the gas will rise a second time. Those gases [referring to the gases first collected in the jar, and which had just been ignited by the electric spark] have disappeared, as you see: their place is vacant, and fresh gas has gone in. Water has been formed from them; and if we repeat our operation, I shall have another vacancy, as you will see by the water rising. I always have an empty vessel after the explosion,

because the vapor or gas into which that water has been resolved by the battery explodes under the influence of the spark, and changes into water; and by and by you will see in this upper vessel some drops of water trickling down the sides and collecting at the bottom.

We are here dealing with water entirely, without reference to the atmosphere. The water of the candle had the atmosphere helping to produce it; but in this way it can be produced independently of the air. Water, therefore, ought to contain that other substance which the candle takes from the air, and which, combining wih the hydrogen, produces water.

Just now you saw that one end of this battery took hold of the copper, extracting it from the vessel which contained the blue solution. It was effected by this wire; and surely we may say, if the battery has such power with a metallic solution which we made and unmade, may we not find that it is possible to split asunder the component parts of the water, and put them into this place and that place? Suppose I take the poles—the metallic ends of this battery—and see what will happen with the water in this apparatus, where we have separated the two ends far apart. I place one here [at A], and the other there [at B], and I

have little shelves with holes which I can put upon each pole, and so arrange them that whatever escapes from the two ends of the battery will appear as separate gases; for you saw that the water did not become vaporous, but gaseous. The wires are now in perfect and proper connection with the vessel containing the water; and you see the bubbles rising: let us collect these bubbles and see what they are. Here is a glass cylinder [O]; I fill it with water and put it over one end [A] of the pile; and I will take another [H] and put it over the other end [B] of the pile. And so now we have a double apparatus, with both places delivering gas. Both these jars will fill with gas. There they go, that to the right [H] filling very rapidly; the one to the left [O] filling not so rapidly; and though I have allowed some bubbles to escape, yet still the action is going on pretty regularly; and

A double apparatus in which the gases produced by the action of the battery on the water are collected in separate cylinders.

were it not that one is rather smaller than the other, you would see that I should have twice as much in this [H] as I have in that [O]. Both these gases are colorless; they stand over the water without condensing; they are alike in all things— I mean in all *apparent* things; and we have here an opportunity of examining these bodies and ascertaining what they are. Their bulk is large, and we can easily apply experiments to them. I will take this jar [H] first, and will ask you to be prepared to recognize hydrogen.

Think of all its qualities—the light gas which stood well in inverted vessels, burning with a pale flame at the mouth of the jar—and see whether this gas does not satisfy all these conditions. If it be hydrogen, it will remain here while I hold this jar inverted. [A light was then applied and the hydrogen burned.] What is there now in the other jar? You know that the two together made an explosive mixture. But what can this be which we find as the other constituent in water, and which must therefore be that stubstance which made the hydrogen burn? We know that the water we put into the vessel consisted of the two things together. We find one of these is hydrogen: what must that other be which was in the water before the experiment, and which we now have by itself? I am

about to put this lighted splinter of wood into the gas. The gas itself will not burn, but it will make the splinter of wood burn. See how it invigorates the combustion of the wood, and how it makes it burn far better than the air would make it burn; and now you see by itself that very other substance which is contained in the water, and which, when the water was formed by the burning of the candle, must have been taken from the atmosphere. What shall we call it, A, B, or C? Let us call it O—call it "oxygen": it is a very good distinct-sounding name. This, then, is the oxygen which was present in the water, forming so large a part of it.

We shall now begin to understand more clearly our experiments and researches; because, when we have examined these things once or twice, we shall soon see why a candle burns in the air. When we have in this way analyzed the water—that is to say, separated, or electrolyzed its parts out of it— we get two volumes of hydrogen, and one of the body that burns it. And these two are represented to us on the diagram which you will find on the following page, with their weights also stated; and we shall find that the oxygen is a very heavy body by comparison with the hydrogen. It is the other element in water.

Hydrogen	Oxygen	Oxygen 88.9
		Hydrogen 11.1
		Water 100.0

I had better, perhaps, tell you now how we get this oxygen abundantly, having shown you how we can separate it from the water. Oxygen, as you will immediately imagine, exists in the atmosphere; for how should the candle burn to produce water without it? Such a thing would be absolutely impossible, and chemically impossible, without oxygen. Can we get it from the air? Well, there are some very complicated and difficult processes by which we can get it from the air; but we have better processes.

There is a substance called black oxide of manganese: it is a very black-looking mineral, but very useful, and when made red-hot it gives out oxygen. Here is an iron bottle which has had some of this substance put into it. There is a tube fixed to it, and a fire ready made, so we shall put that retort into the fire, for it is made of iron, and can stand the heat. Here is a salt called chlorate of potassa, which is now made in large quantities for bleaching, and chemical and medical uses, and for pyro-

technic and other purposes. I will take some and mix it with some of the oxide of manganese (oxide of copper, or oxide of iron would do as well); and if I put these together in a retort, far less than a red heat is sufficient to evolve this oxygen from the mixture. I am not preparing to make much, because we want only sufficient for our experiments; only, as you will see immediately, if I use too small a charge, the first portion of the gas will be mixed with the air already in the retort, and I should be obliged to sacrifice the first portion of the gas, because it would be so much diluted with air; the first portion must therefore be thrown away. You will find in this case, that a common spirit lamp is quite sufficient for me to get the oxygen, and so we shall have two processes going on for its preparation. See how freely the gas is coming over from that small portion of the mixture.

A mixture of black oxide of manganese and chlorate of potassa is heated to produce oxygen.

We will examine it, and see what are its properties. Now, in this way we are producing, as you will observe, a gas just like the one we had in the experiment with the battery, transparent, undissolved by water, and presenting the ordinary visible properties of the atmosphere. (As this first jar contains the air, together with the first portions of the oxygen set free during the preparation, we will carry it out of the way, and be prepared to make our experiments in a regular, dignified manner.) And, inasmuch as that power of making wood, wax, or other things burn, was so marked in the oxygen we obtained by means of the voltaic battery from water, we may expect to find the same property here. We will try it. You see there is the combustion of a lighted taper in air, and here is its combustion in this gas. See how brightly and how beautifully it burns! You can also see more than

The flame of a lighted taper becomes brighter when it is placed in a jar of oxygen.

this—you will perceive it is a heavy gas, whilst the hydrogen would go up like a balloon, or even faster than a balloon, when not encumbered with the weight of the envelope. You may easily see that although we obtained from water twice as much in volume of the hydrogen as of oxygen, it does not follow that we have twice as much in weight —because one is heavy, and the other a very light gas. We have means of weighing gases or air; but without stopping to explain that, let me just tell you what their respective weights are. The weight of a pint of hydrogen is three quarters of a grain; the weight of the same quantity of oxygen is nearly twelve grains. This is a very great difference. The weight of a cubic foot of hydrogen is one twelfth of an ounce; and the weight of a cubic foot of oxygen is one ounce and a third. And so on we might come to masses of matter which may be weighed in the balance, and which we can take account of as to hundredweights and as to tons, as you will see almost immediately.

	HYDROGEN	OXYGEN
1 pint	3/4 grain	12 grains
1 cu.ft.	1/12 ounce	1 1/3 ounces

Now, as regards this very property of oxygen supporting combustion, which we may compare to air, I will take a piece of candle to show it to you in a rough way, and the result will be rough. There is our candle burning in the air: how will it burn in oxygen? I have here a jar of this gas, and I am about to put it over the candle for you to compare the action of this gas with that of the air. Why, look at it: it looks something like the light you saw at the poles of the voltaic battery. Think how vigorous that action must be! And yet, during all that action, nothing more is produced than what is produced by the burning of the candle in air. We have the same production of water, and the same phenomena exactly, when we use this gas instead of air, as we have when the candle is burned in air.

But now we have got a knowledge of this new substance, we can look at it a little more distinctly, in order to satisfy ourselves that we have got a good general understanding of this part of the product of a candle. It is wonderful how great the supporting powers of this substance are as regards combustion. For instance, here is a lamp which, simple though it be, is the original, I may say, of a great variety of lamps which are constructed for divers purposes—for lighthouses,

microscopic illuminations, and other uses; and if it were proposed to make it burn very brightly, you would say, "If a candle burned better in oxygen, will not a lamp do the same?" Why, it will do so.

Here is a tube from our oxygen reservoir, and I am about to apply it to this flame, which I will previously make burn badly on purpose. There comes the oxygen: what a combustion that makes! But if I shut it off, what becomes of the lamp? [The lamp then relapsed to its former dimness.] It is wonderful how, by means of oxygen, we get combustion accelerated. But it does not affect merely the combustion of hydrogen, or carbon, or the candle; it exalts all combustions of the common kind. We will take one which relates to iron, for instance, as you have already seen iron burn a little in the atmosphere. Here is a jar of oxygen, and this is a piece of iron wire; but if it were a bar as thick as my wrist, it would burn the same. I first attach a little piece of wood to the iron, I then set the wood on fire, and let them both down together into the jar. The wood is now alight, and there it burns as wood should burn in oxygen; but it will soon communicate its combustion to the iron. The iron is now burning brilliantly, and will continue so for a long time. As long as we supply oxygen, so

Oxygen in the jar accelerates the combustion of the iron wire.

long can we carry on the combustion of the iron, until the latter is consumed.

We will now put that on one side, and take a piece of sulphur—you know how sulphur burns in the air—well, we put it into the oxygen, and you will see that whatever can burn in air, can burn with a far greater intensity in oxygen, leading you to think that perhaps the atmosphere itself owes all its power of combustion to this gas. The sulphur is now burning very quietly in the oxygen; but you cannot for a moment mistake the very high and increased action which takes place when it is so burned, instead of being burned merely in common air.

I am now about to show you the combustion of another substance—phosphorus. I can do it better for you here than you can do it at home. This is a very combustible substance; and if it be so combustible in air, what might you expect it

would be in oxygen? I am about to show it to you not in its fullest intensity, for if I did so we should almost blow the apparatus up—I may even now crack the jar, though I do not want to break things carelessly. You see how it burns in the air. But what a glorious light it gives out when I introduce it into oxygen. There you see the solid particles going off which cause that combustion to be so brilliantly luminous.

Thus far we have tested this power of oxygen, and the high combustion it produces by means of other substances. We must now, for a little while longer, look at it as respects the hydrogen. You know, when we allowed the oxygen and the hydrogen derived from the water to mix and burn together, we had a little explosion. You remember, also, that when I burned the oxygen and the hydrogen in a jet together, we got very little light, but great heat. I am now about to set fire to oxygen and hydrogen, mixed in the proportion in which they occur in water. Here is a vessel containing one volume of oxygen and two volumes of hydrogen. This mixture is exactly of the same nature as the gas we just now obtained from the voltaic battery: it would be far too much to burn at once; I have therefore arranged to blow soap bubbles with it, and burn those bubbles, that we

may see by a general experiment or two how this oxygen supports the combustion of the hydrogen. First of all, we will see whether we can blow a bubble. Well, there goes the gas. Here I have a bubble. I am receiving them on my hand: and you will perhaps think I am acting oddly in this experiment; but it is to show you that we must not always trust to noise and sounds, but rather to real facts [exploding a bubble on the palm of his hand]. I am afraid to fire a bubble from the end of the pipe, because the explosion would pass up into the jar and blow it to pieces. This oxygen then will unite with the hydrogen, as you see by the phenomena, and hear by the sound, with the utmost readiness of action, and all its powers are then taken up in its neutralization of the qualities of the hydrogen.

So now I think you will perceive the whole history of water with reference to oxygen and the air, from what we have before said. Why does a piece of potassium decompose water? Because it finds oxygen in the water. What is set free when I put it in the water, as I am about to do again? It sets free hydrogen, and the hydrogen burns; but the potassium itself combines with oxygen; and this piece of potassium, in taking the water apart —the water, you may say, derived from the com-

bustion of the candle—takes away the oxygen which the candle took from the air, and so sets the hydrogen free; and even if I take a piece of ice, and put a piece of potassium upon it, the beautiful affinities by which the oxygen and the hydrogen are related are such, that the ice will absolutely set fire to the potassium. I show this to you today, in order to enlarge your ideas of these things, and that you may see how greatly results are modified by circumstances. There is the potassium on the ice, producing a sort of volcanic action.

It will be my place in the next lecture, having pointed out these anomalous actions, to show you that none of these extra and strange effects are met with by us—that none of these strange and injurious actions take place when we are burning, not merely a candle, but gas in our streets, or fuel in our fireplaces—so long as we confine ourselves within the laws that Nature has made for our guidance.

LECTURE V

The Nature of the Atmosphere

WE HAVE now seen that we can produce hydrogen and oxygen from the water that we obtained from the candle. Hydrogen, you know, comes from the candle, and oxygen, you believe, comes from the air. But then you have a right to ask me, "How is it that the air and the oxygen do not equally well burn the candle?" If you remember what happened when I put a jar of oxygen over a piece of candle, you recollect there was a very different kind of combustion to that which took place in the air. Now, why is this? It is a very important question: it relates most in-

timately to the nature of the atmosphere, and is most important to us.

We have several tests for oxygen besides the mere burning of bodies. You have seen a candle burned in oxygen, or in the air; you have seen phosphorus burned in the air, or in oxygen; and you have seen iron wire burned in oxygen. But we have other tests besides these, and I am about to refer to one or two of them for the purpose of carrying your conviction and your experience further. Here we have a vessel of oxygen. I will show its presence to you: if I take a lighted stick and put it into that oxygen, you know, by a previous experiment, what will happen; if I put that stick into the jar, it will tell you whether we have oxygen here or not. Yes! We have proved it by combustion.

Now here is another test for oxygen, which is a very curious and useful one. I have here two jars full of gas, with a plate between them to prevent their mixing; I take the plate away, and the gases are creeping one into the other. "What happens?" say you: "they together produce no such combustion as was seen in the case of the candle." But see how the presence of oxygen is told by its association with this other substance.[15] What a beautifully colored gas I have obtained in this way,

showing me the presence of the oxygen! In the same way we can try this experiment by mixing common air with this nitrous oxide. Here is a jar containing air—such air as the candle would burn in—and here is a jar or bottle containing the test gas. I let them come together over water, and you see the result: the contents of the test bottle are flowing into the jar of air, and you see I obtain exactly the same kind of action as before, and that shows me that there is oxygen in the air—the very same substance that has been already obtained by us from the water produced by the candle.

But then, beyond that, how is it that the candle does not burn in air as well as in oxygen? We will come to that point at once. I have here two jars; they are filled to the same height with gas, and the appearance to the eye is alike in both, and I really do not know at present which of these jars contains oxygen and which contains air, although I know they have previously been filled with these gases. But here is our test gas, and I am going to work with the two jars, in order to examine whether there is any difference between them in the quality of reddening this gas. I am now going to turn this test gas into one of the jars, and observe what happens. There is reddening, you see; there is then oxygen present. We will now test the

other jar; but you see this is not so distinctly red as the first: and, further, this curious thing happens—if I take these two gases and shake them well together with water, we shall absorb the red gas; and then, if I put in more of this test gas and shake again, we shall absorb more; and I can go on as long as there be any oxygen present to produce that effect. If I let in air, it will not matter; but the moment I introduce water, the red gas disappears; and I may go on in this way, putting in more and more of the test gas, until I come to something left behind which will not redden any longer by the use of that particular body that rendered the air and the oxygen red.

Why is that? You will see in a moment it is because there is, besides oxygen, something else present which is left behind. I will let a little more air into the jar, and if it turns red you will know that some of that reddening gas is still present, and that consequently it was not for the want of this producing body that that air was left behind.

Now, you will begin to understand what I am about to say. You saw that when I burned phosphorus in a jar, as the smoke produced by the phosphorus and the oxygen of the air condensed, it left a good deal of gas unburned, just as this red gas left something untouched—there was, in

fact, this gas left behind, which the phosphorus cannot touch, which the reddening gas cannot touch, and this something is not oxygen, and yet is part of the atmosphere.

So that is one way of opening out air into the two things of which it is composed—oxygen, which burns our candles, our phosphorus, or anything else; and this other substance—nitrogen—which will not burn them. This other part of the air is by far the larger proportion, and it is a very curious body, when we come to examine it; it is remarkably curious, and yet you say, perhaps, that it is very uninteresting. It is uninteresting in some respects because of this—that it shows no brilliant effects of combustion. If I test it with a taper as I do oxygen and hydrogen, it does not burn like hydrogen, nor does it make the taper burn like oxygen. Try it in any way I will, it does neither the one thing nor the other: it will not take fire; it will not let the taper burn; it puts out the combustion of everything. There is nothing that will burn in it in common circumstances. It has no smell; it is not sour; it does not dissolve in water; it is neither an acid nor an alkali; it is as indifferent to all our organs as it is possible for a thing to be.

You might say, "It is nothing; it is not worth chemical attention; what does it do in the air?"

Ah! then come our beautiful and fine results shown us by an observant philosophy. Suppose, in place of having nitrogen, or nitrogen and oxygen, we had pure oxygen as our atmosphere; what would become of us? You know very well that a piece of iron lit in a jar of oxygen goes on burning to the end. When you see a fire in an iron grate, imagine where the grate would go to if the whole of the atmosphere were oxygen. The grate would burn up more powerfully than the coals—for the iron of the grate itself is even more combustible than the coals which we burn in it. A fire put into the middle of a locomotive would be a fire in a magazine of fuel, if the atmosphere were oxygen. The nitrogen lowers it down and makes it moderate and useful for us, and then, with all that, it takes away with it the fumes that you have seen produced from the candle, disperses them throughout the whole of the atmosphere, and carries them away to places where they are wanted to perform a great and glorious purpose of good to man, for the sustenance of vegetation; and thus does a most wonderful work, although you say, on examining it, "Why, it is a perfectly indifferent thing." This nitrogen in its ordinary state is an inactive element; no action short of the most intense electric force, and then in the most infinitely

small degree, can cause the nitrogen to combine directly with the other element of the atmosphere, or with other things round about it; it is a perfectly indifferent, and therefore to say, a safe substance.

But before I take you to that result, I must tell you about the atmosphere itself. Here is the composition of one hundred parts of atmospheric air:

	Bulk	Weight
Oxygen	20	22.3
Nitrogen	80	77.7
	100	100.0

It is a true analysis of the atmosphere, so far as regards the quantity of oxygen and the quantity of nitrogen present. By our analysis, we find that 5 pints of the atmosphere contain only 1 pint of oxygen, and 4 pints, or 4 parts, of nitrogen by bulk. That is our analysis of the atmosphere. It requires all that quantity of nitrogen to reduce the oxygen down, so as to be able to supply the candle properly with fuel, so as to supply us with an atmosphere which our lungs can healthily and safely breathe; for it is just as important to make the oxygen right for us to breathe, as it is to make the atmosphere right for the burning of the fire and the candle.

But now for this atmosphere. First of all, let me tell you the weight of these gases. A pint of nitrogen weighs 10 4/10 grains, or a cubic foot weighs 1 1/6 ounces. That is the weight of the nitrogen. The oxygen is heavier: a pint of it weighs 11 9/10 grains, and a cubic foot weighs 1 3/4 ounces. A pint of air weighs about 10 7/10 grains, and a cubic foot 1 1/5 ounces.

5 PINTS OF ATMOSPHERE contain		
1 PINT OF OXYGEN	4 PINTS OF NITROGEN	

	NITROGEN	OXYGEN	AIR
1 pint	10 4/14 gr.	11 9/10 gr.	10 7/10 gr.
1 cu. ft.	1 1/6 oz.	1 3/4 oz.	1 1/5 oz.

You have asked me several times, and I am very glad you have, "How do you weigh gases?" I will show you; it is very simple, and easily done. Here is a balance, and here a copper bottle, made as light as we can consistent with due strength, turned very nicely in the lathe, and made perfectly airtight, with a stopcock, which we can open and shut, which at present is open, and therefore allows the bottle to be full of air. I have here a nicely

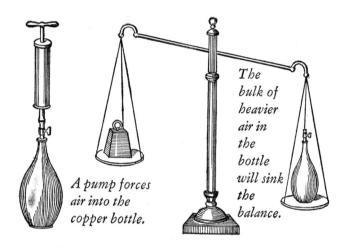

A pump forces air into the copper bottle.

The bulk of heavier air in the bottle will sink the balance.

adjusted balance, in which I think the bottle, in its present condition, will be balanced by the weight on the other side. And here is a pump by which we can force the air into this bottle, and with it we will force in a certain number of volumes of air, as measured by the pump. We will shut that in and put it in the balance. See how it sinks: it is much heavier than it was. By what? By the air that we have forced into it by the pump. There is not a greater *bulk* of air, but there is the same bulk of *heavier* air, because we have forced in air upon it. And that you may have a fair notion in your mind as to how much this air measures, here is a jar full of water. We will open that copper vessel into this jar, and let the air

return to its former state. All I have to do now is to screw them tightly together, and to turn the taps, when there, you see, is the bulk of the twenty pumps of air which I forced into the bottle; and to make sure that we have been quite correct in what we have been doing, we will take the bottle again to the balance, and if it is now counterpoised by the original weight, we shall be quite sure we have made our experiment correctly. It is balanced; so, you see, we can find out the weight of the extra volumes of air forced in, in that way, and by that means we are able to ascertain that a cubic foot of air weighs 1 1/5 ounces.

But that small experiment will by no means convey to your mind the whole literal truth of this matter. It is wonderful how it accumulates when you come to larger volumes. This bulk of air weighs 1 1/5 ounces. What do you think of the contents of that box above there, which I have had made for the purpose? The air which is within that box weighs one pound—a full pound; and I have calculated the weight of the air in this room —you would hardly imagine it, but it is above a ton. So rapidly do the weights rise up, and so important is the presence of the atmosphere, and of the oxygen and the nitrogen in it, and the use it performs in conveying things to and fro from

place to place, and carrying bad vapors to places where they will do good instead of harm.

Having given you that little illustration with respect to the weight of the air, let me show you certain consequences of it. You have a right to them, because you would not understand so much without it. Suppose I take a pump somewhat similar to the one I had a little while ago to force air into the bottle, and suppose I place it in such a manner that by certain arrangements I can apply my hand to it: my hand moves about in the air so easily that it seems to feel nothing, and I can hardly get velocity enough by any motion of my own in the atmosphere to make sure that there is much resistance to it. But, when I put my hand here [on the pump intake, which was afterward exhausted], you see what happens. Why is my

The weight of the atmosphere above fastens the hand to the pump intake from which the air has been exhausted.

When the air is pumped from the glass, the bladder stretched across the top will be pushed down by the weight of the air above until it eventually breaks.

hand fastened to this place, and why am I able to pull this pump about? And see! how is it that I can hardly get my hand away? Why is this? It is the weight of the air—the weight of the air that is above. I have another experiment here, which I think will explain to you more about it. When the air is pumped from underneath the bladder which is stretched over this glass, you will see the effect in another shape: the top is quite flat at present, but I will make a very little motion with the pump, and now look at it—see how it has gone down, see how it is bent in. You will see the bladder go in more and more, until at last I expect it will be driven in and broken by the force of the atmosphere pressing upon it. [The bladder at last broke with a loud report.] Now, that was done entirely by the weight of the air pressing on it,

and you can easily understand how that is. The particles that are piled up in the atmosphere stand upon each other, as these five cubes do. You can easily conceive that four of these five cubes are resting upon the bottom one, and if I take that away, the others will all sink down. So it is with the atmosphere: the air that is above is sustained by the air that is beneath; and when the air is pumped away from beneath them, the change occurs which you saw when I placed my hand on the air pump, and which you saw in the case of the bladder, and which you shall see better here.

I have tied over this jar a piece of sheet rubber, and I am now about to take away the air from the inside of the jar; and if you will watch the rubber sheet—which acts as a partition between the air below and the air above—you will see, when I pump, how the pressure shows itself. See where it is going to—I can actually put my hand into the jar; and yet this result is only caused by the great and powerful action of the air above. How beautifully it shows this curious circumstance!

Here is something else—a little apparatus of two hollow brass hemispheres, closely fitted together, and having connected with it a pipe and a cock, through which we can exhaust the air from the inside; and although the two halves are so

The hemispheres cannot be pulled apart when the air from the inside has been exhausted.

easily taken apart, while the air is left within, yet you will see, when we exhaust it by and by, no power of any two of you will be able to pull them apart. Every square inch of surface that is contained in the area of that vessel sustains fifteen pounds by weight, or nearly so, when the air is taken out.

Here is another very pretty thing—the boys' sucker, only refined by the philosopher. We have a perfect right to take toys, and make them into philosophy, inasmuch as nowadays we are turning philosophy into toys. Here is a sucker, only it is made of India rubber: if I clap it upon the table, you see at once it holds. Why does it hold? I can slip it about, and yet if I try to pull it up, it seems as if it would pull the table with it. I can easily make it slip about from place to place; but only when I bring it to the edge of the table can I get it

off. It is only kept down by the pressure of the atmosphere above. We have a couple of them; and if you take these two and press them together, you will see how firmly they stick. And, indeed, we may use them as they are proposed to be used, to stick against windows, or against walls, where they will adhere for an evening, and serve to hang anything on that you want.

This next is a very pretty experiment in illustration of the pressure of the atmosphere. Here is a tumbler of water. Suppose I were to ask you to turn that tumbler upside down, so that the water should not fall out, and yet not be kept in by your hand, but merely by using the pressure of the atmosphere. Could you do that? Take a small glass, either quite full or half full of water, and put a flat card on the top, turn it upside down, and then see what becomes of the card and of the water. The air cannot get in because the water by its capillary attraction round the edge keeps it out.

I think this will give you a correct notion of what you may call the materiality of the air; and when I tell you that the box holds a pound of it, and this room more than a ton, you will begin to think that air is something very serious. I will make another experiment, to convince you of this positive resistance. There is that beautiful ex-

periment of the popgun, made so well and so
easily, you know, out of a quill, or a tube, or any-
thing of that kind—where we take a slice of po-
tato, for instance, or an apple, and take the tube
and cut out a pellet, as I have now done, and
push it to one end. I have made that end tight;
and now I take another piece and put it in: it will
confine the air that is within the tube perfectly
and completely for our purpose; and I shall now

*The popgun experiment, demonstrating
the positive resistance of the air.*

find it absolutely impossible by any force of mine
to drive that little pellet close up to the other. It
cannot be done. I may press the air to a certain
extent, but if I go on pressing, long before it
comes to the second, the confined air will drive the
front one out with a force something like that of
gunpowder; for gunpowder is in part dependent
upon the same action that you see here exemplified.

I saw the other day an experiment which pleased
me much, as I thought it would serve our purpose
here. (I ought to have held my tongue for four or
five minutes before beginning this experiment, be-
cause it depends upon my lungs for success.) By

the proper application of air I expect to be able to drive this egg out of one cup into the other by the force of my breath; but if I fail, it is in a good cause; and I do not promise success, because I have been talking more than I ought to do to make the experiment succeed.

[The Lecturer succeeded in blowing the egg from one cup to another.]

You see that the air which I blow goes downwards between the egg and the cup, and makes a blast under the egg, and is thus able to lift a heavy thing—for a full egg is a very heavy thing for air to lift. If you want to make the experiment, you had better boil the egg quite hard first, and then you may very safely try to blow it from one cup to the other, with a little care.

I have now kept you long enough upon this property of the weight of the air, but there is another thing I should like to mention. You saw the way in which, in this popgun, I was able to drive the second piece of potato half or two thirds of an inch before the first piece started, by virtue of the elasticity of the air—just as I pressed into the copper bottle the particles of air by means of the pump. Now, this depends upon a wonderful property in the air, namely, its elasticity; and I should like to give you a good illustration of this. If I

take anything that confines the air properly, as
this membrane, which also is able to contract and
expand so as to give us a measure of the elasticity
of the air, and confine in this bladder a certain por-
tion of air; and then, if we take the atmosphere off
from the outside of it, just as in these cases we put
the pressure on—if we take the pressure off, you
will see how it will then go on expanding and ex-
panding, larger and larger, until it will fill the
whole of this bell jar, showing you that wonderful
property of the air, its elasticity, its compressi-
bility, and expansibility, to an exceedingly large
extent, and which is very essential for the purposes
and services it performs in the economy of crea-
tion.

When the pressure of the atmosphere is removed from within the bell jar, the air inside the bladder expands.

We will now turn to another very important part of our subject, remembering that we have examined the candle in its burning, and have found that it gives rise to various products. We have the products, you know, of soot, of water, and of something else which you have not yet examined. We have collected the water, but have allowed the other things to go into the air. Let us now examine some of these other products.

Here is an experiment which I think will help you in part in this way. We will put our candle there, and place over it a chimney, thus. I think my candle will go on burning, because the air passage is open at the bottom and the top. In the first place, you see the moisture appearing—that you know about. It is water produced from the candle by the action of the air upon its hydrogen. But, besides that, something is going out at the top: it is not moisture—it is not water—it is not condensable; and yet, after all, it has very singular properties. You will find that the air coming out of the top of our chimney is nearly sufficient to blow the light out I am holding to it; and if I put the light fairly opposed to the current, it will blow it quite out. You will say that is as it should be; and I am supposing that you think it ought to do so, because the nitrogen does not support combustion,

A light held near the current of air coming out of the top of the chimney will be blown out.

and ought to put the candle out, since the candle will not burn in nitrogen. But is there nothing else there than nitrogen? I must now anticipate—that is to say, I must use my own knowledge to supply you with the means that we adopt for the purpose of ascertaining these things, and examining such gases as these. I will take an empty bottle —here is one—and if I hold it over this chimney, I shall get the combustion of the candle below sending its results into the bottle above; and we shall soon find that this bottle contains not merely an air that is bad as regards the combustion of a taper put into it, but having other properties.

Let me take a little quicklime and pour some common water on to it—the commonest water will do. I will stir it a moment, then pour it upon a piece of filtering paper in a funnel, and we shall

very quickly have a clear water proceeding to the bottle below, as I have here. I have plenty of this water in another bottle; but, nevertheless, I should like to use the limewater that was prepared before you, so that you may see what its uses are. If I take some of this beautiful clear limewater, and pour it into this jar, which has collected the air from the candle, you will see a change coming about. Do you see that the water has become quite milky? Observe, that will not happen with air merely.

Here is a bottle filled with air; and if I put some limewater into it, neither the oxygen nor the nitrogen, nor anything else that is in that quantity of air, will make any change in the limewater. It remains perfectly clear, and no shaking of that quantity of limewater with that quantity of air in its common state will cause any change; but if I take this bottle with the limewater, and hold it so as to get the general products of the candle in contact with it, in a very short time we shall have it milky. There is the chalk, consisting of the lime which we used in making the limewater, combined with something that came from the candle—that other product which we are in search of, and which I want to tell you about today.

This is a substance made visible to us by its action, which is not the action of the limewater

either upon the oxygen or upon the nitrogen, nor upon the water itself, but it is something new to us from the candle. And then we find this white powder, produced by the limewater and the vapor from the candle, appears to us very much like whitening or chalk, and, when examined, it does prove to be exactly the same substance as whitening or chalk. So we are led, or have been led, to observe upon the various circumstances of this experiment, and to trace this production of chalk to its various causes, to give us the true knowledge of the nature of this combustion of the candle—to find that this substance, issuing from the candle, is exactly the same as that substance which would issue from a retort, if I were to put some pure chalk into it with a little moisture, and make it red-hot; you would then find that exactly the same substance would issue from it as from the candle.

But we have a better means of getting this substance, and in greater quantity, so as to ascertain what its general characters are. We find this substance in very great abundance in a multitude of cases where you would least expect it. All limestones contain a great deal of this gas which issues from the candle, and which we call *carbonic acid*.[16] All chalks, all shells, all corals contain a great

quantity of this curious air. We find it fixed in these stones; for which reason Dr. Black called it "fixed air"—finding it in these fixed things like marble and chalk. He called it fixed air, because it lost its quality of air, and assumed the condition of a solid body. We can easily get this air from marble. Here is a jar containing a little muriatic acid, and here is a taper which, if I put it into another jar, will show only the presence of common air. There is, you see, pure air down to the bottom; the jar is full of it. Here is a substance—marble,[17] a very beautiful and superior marble—and if I put these pieces of marble into the jar, a great boiling apparently goes on. That, however, is not steam— it is a gas that is rising up; and if I now search the jar by a candle, I shall have exactly the same effect produced upon the taper as I had from the air which issued from the end of the chimney over the burning candle. It is exactly the same action, and caused by the very same substance that issued from the candle; and in this way we can get carbonic acid gas in great abundance. We also find that this gas is not merely contained in marble. Here is a vessel in which I have put some common whitening—chalk, which has been washed in water and deprived of its coarser particles, and so supplied to the plasterer as whitening. Here is a

large jar containing this whitening and water, and I have here some strong sulphuric acid, which is the acid you might have to use if you were to make these experiments (only, in using this acid with limestone, the body that is produced is an insoluble substance, whereas the muriatic acid produces a soluble substance that does not so much thicken the water). And you will seek out a reason why I take this kind of apparatus for the purpose of showing this experiment. I do it because you may repeat in a small way what I am about to do in a large one. You will have here just the same kind of action; and I am evolving in this large jar carbonic acid, exactly the same in its nature and properties as the gas which we obtained from the combustion of the candle in the atmosphere. And no matter how different the two methods by which we prepare this carbonic acid, you will see, when we get

The action of the chalk and sulphuric acid in water produces carbonic acid gas.

to the end of our subject, that it is all exactly the same, whether prepared in the one way or in the other.

We will now proceed to the next experiment with regard to this gas. What is its nature? Here is one of the vessels full, and we will try it, as we have done so many other gases, by combustion. You see it is not combustible, nor does it support combustion. Neither, as we know, does it dissolve much in water, because we collect it over water very easily. Then, you know that it has an effect, and becomes white in contact with limewater; and when it does become white in that way, it becomes one of the constituents to make carbonate of lime or limestone.

The next thing I must show you is, that it really does dissolve a little in water, and therefore that it is unlike oxygen and hydrogen in that respect. I have here an apparatus by which we can produce this solution. In the lower part of this apparatus is marble and acid, and in the upper part cold water. The valves are so arranged that the gas can get from one to the other. I will set it in action now, and you can see the gas bubbling up through the water, as it has been doing all night long, and by this time we shall find that we have this substance dissolved in the water. If I take a

glass and draw off some of the water, I find that it tastes a little acid to the mouth: it is impregnated with carbonic acid; and if I now apply a little limewater to it, that will give us a test of its presence. This water will make the limewater turbid and white, which is proof of the presence of carbonic acid.

Then it is a very weighty gas—it is heavier than the atmosphere. I have put their respective weights at the lower part of this table, along with, for comparison, the weights of the other gases we have been examining:—

	Pint	Cubic Foot
Hydrogen	3/4 grains	1/12 ounces
Oxygen	11 9/10 "	1 1/3 "
Nitrogen	10 4/10 "	1 1/6 "
Air	10 7/10 "	1 1/5 "
Carbonic acid	16 1/3 "	1 9/10 "

A pint of it weighs 16 1/3 grains, and a cubic foot weighs 1 9/10 ounces, almost two ounces. You can see by many experiments that this is a heavy gas. Suppose I take a glass containing nothing else but air, and from this vessel containing the carbonic acid I attempt to pour a little of this gas into that glass; I wonder whether any has gone in or not. I cannot tell by the appearance, but I

can in this way. [The Lecturer introduced a taper which went out.] Yes, there it is, you see; and if I were to examine it by limewater, I should find it by that test also. I will take this little bucket, and put it down into the well of carbonic acid—indeed, we too often have real wells of carbonic acid—and now, if there is any carbonic acid, I must have got to it by this time, and it will be in this bucket, which we will examine with a taper. There it is, you see; it is full of carbonic acid.

There is another experiment by which I will show you its weight. I have here a jar suspended at one end of a balance—it is now equipoised; but when I pour this carbonic acid into the jar on the one side which now contains air, you will see it sink down at once, because of the carbonic acid that I pour into it. And now, if I examine this jar with the lighted taper, I shall find that the carbonic acid has fallen into it, and it no longer has any power

The weight of carbonic acid gas is measured by pouring it into a jar of air suspended at one end of a balance.

A soap bubble or balloon filled with air floats on carbonic acid gas. This proves that the gas is heavier than air.

of supporting the combustion. If I blow a soap bubble, which of course will be filled with air, and let it fall into this jar of carbonic acid, it will float. But I shall first of all take one of these little balloons filled with air. I am not quite sure where the carbonic acid is; we will just try the depth, and see whereabouts is its level. There, you see, we have this bladder floating on the carbonic acid; and if I evolve some more of the carbonic acid, the bladder will be lifted up higher. There it goes —the jar is nearly full; and now I will see whether I can blow a soap bubble on that, and float it in the same way. It is floating, as the balloon floated, by virtue of the greater weight of the carbonic acid than of the air. And now, having so far given you the history of the carbonic acid—as to its sources in the candle, as to its physical properties and weight—in the next lecture I shall show you of what it is composed, and where it gets its elements from.

LECTURE VI

Respiration and Its Analogy to the Burning of a Candle

I TOLD you, when we last met, a good deal about carbonic acid. We found, by the limewater test, that when the vapor from the top of the candle or lamp was received into bottles, and tested by this solution of limewater, we had that white opacity which was in fact calcareous matter, like shells and corals, and many of the rocks and minerals in the earth. But I have not yet told you fully and clearly the chemical history of this substance—

carbonic acid—as we have it from the candle, and I must now resume that subject. We have seen the products, and the nature of them, as they issue from the candle. We have traced the water to its elements, and now we have to see where are the elements of the carbonic acid supplied by the candle. A few experiments will show this.

You remember that when a candle burns badly, it produces smoke; but if it is burning well, there is no smoke. And you know that the brightness of the candle is due to this smoke, which becomes ignited. Here is an experiment to prove this: so long as the smoke remains in the flame of the candle and becomes ignited, it gives a beautiful light, and never appears to us in the form of black particles. I will light some fuel, which is extravagant in its burning. This will serve our purpose—a little turpentine on a sponge. You see the smoke rising from it, and floating into the air in large quantities; and, remember now, the carbonic acid that we have from the candle is from such smoke as that. To make that evident to you, I will introduce this turpentine burning on the sponge into a flask where I have plenty of oxygen, the rich part of the atmosphere, and you now see that the smoke is all consumed. This is the first part of our experiment; and now, what follows? The carbon which you

saw flying off from the turpentine flame in the air is now entirely burned in this oxygen, and we shall find that it will, by this rough and temporary experiment, give us exactly the same conclusion and result as we had from the combustion of the candle. The reason why I make the experiment in this manner is solely that I may cause the steps of our demonstration to be so simple that you can never for a moment lose the train of reasoning, if you only pay attention. All the carbon which is burned in oxygen, or air, comes out as carbonic acid, whilst those particles which are not so burned show you the second substance in the carbonic acid—namely, the carbon—that body which made the flame so bright whilst there was plenty of air, but which was thrown off in excess when there was not oxygen enough to burn it.

I have also to show you a little more distinctly the history of carbon and oxygen, in their union to make carbonic acid. You are now better able to understand this than before, and I have prepared three or four experiments by way of illustration. This jar is filled with oxygen, and here is some carbon which has been placed in a crucible, for the purpose of being made red-hot. I keep my jar dry, and venture to give you a result imperfect in some degree, in order that I may make the experi-

ment brighter. I am about to put the oxygen and the carbon together. That this is carbon (common charcoal pulverized), you will see by the way in which it burns in the air. I am now about to burn it in oxygen, and look at the difference. It may appear to you at a distance as if it were burning with a flame; but it is not so. Every little piece of charcoal is burning as a spark, and whilst it so burns it is producing carbonic acid. I specially want these two or three experiments to point out what I shall dwell upon more distinctly by and by —that carbon burns in this way, and not as a flame.

Instead of taking many particles of carbon to burn, I will take a rather large piece, which will enable you to see the form and size, and to trace the effects very decidedly. Here is the jar of oxygen, and here is the piece of charcoal, to which I have fastened a little piece of wood, which I can set fire to, and so commence the combustion, which I could not conveniently do without. You now see the charcoal burning, but not as a flame (or if there be a flame, it is the smallest possible one, which I know the cause of—namely, the formation of a little carbonic oxide close upon the surface of the carbon). It goes on burning, you see, slowly producing carbonic acid by the union of this carbon or charcoal (they are equivalent terms)

A piece of charcoal burning in a jar of oxygen produces carbonic acid gas.

with the oxygen. I have here another piece of charcoal, a piece of bark, which has the quality of being blown to pieces—exploding as it burns. By the effect of the heat, we shall reduce the lump of carbon into particles that will fly off; still every particle, equally with the whole mass, burns in this peculiar way: it burns as a coal, and not like a flame. You observe a multitude of little combustions going on, but no flame. I do not know a finer experiment than this, to show that carbon burns with a spark.

Here, then, is carbonic acid formed from its elements. It is produced at once; and if we examined it by limewater, you will see that we have the same substance which I have previously described to you. By putting together 6 parts of carbon by weight (whether it comes from the flame of a candle or from powdered charcoal) and 16 parts of oxygen by weight, we have 22 parts of carbonic acid; and, as we saw last time, the 22 parts of car-

bonic acid, combined with 28 parts of lime, pro-
duced common carbonate of lime. If you were to
examine an oyster shell, and weigh the component
parts, you would find that every 50 parts would
give 6 of carbon and 16 of oxygen, combined with
28 of lime. However, I do not want to trouble you
with these minutiae—it is only the general phi-
losophy of the matter that we can now go into. See
how finely the carbon is dissolving away. You
may say that the charcoal is actually dissolving in
the air round about; and if that were perfectly
pure charcoal, which we can easily prepare, there
would be no residue whatever. When we have a
perfectly cleansed and purified piece of carbon,
there is no ash left. The carbon burns as a solid
dense body, that heat alone cannot change as to
its solidity, and yet it passes away into vapor that
never condenses into solid or liquid under ordinary
circumstances; and what is more curious still, is
the fact that the oxygen does not change in its
bulk by the solution of the carbon in it. Just as
the bulk is at first, so it is at last, only it has become
carbonic acid.

There is another experiment which I must give
you before you are fully acquainted with the gen-
eral nature of carbonic acid. Being a compound
body, consisting of carbon and oxygen, carbonic

acid is a body that we ought to be able to take asunder. And so we can. As we did with water, so we can with carbonic acid—take the two parts asunder. The simplest and quickest way is to act upon the carbonic acid by a substance that can attract the oxygen from it, and leave the carbon behind. You recollect that I took potassium and put it upon water or ice, and you saw that it could take the oxygen from the hydrogen. Now, suppose we do something of the same kind here with this carbonic acid. You know carbonic acid to be a heavy gas. I will not test it with limewater, as that will interfere with our subsequent experiments; but I think the heaviness of the gas and the power of extinguishing flame will be sufficient for our purpose. I introduce a flame into the gas, and you will see whether it will be put out. You see the light is extinguished. Indeed, the gas may, perhaps, put out phosphorus, which, you know, has a pretty strong combustion. Here is a piece of phosphorus heated to a high degree. I introduce it into gas, and you observe the light is put out; but it will take fire again in the air, because there it re-enters into combustion. Now, let me take a piece of potassium, a substance which, even at common temperatures, can act upon carbonic acid, though not sufficiently for our present purpose, because it

soon gets covered with a protecting coat; but if we warm it up to the burning point in air, as we have a fair right to do, and as we have done with phosphorus, you will see that it can burn in carbonic acid; and if it burns, it will burn by taking oxygen, so that you will see what is left behind. I am going, then, to burn this potassium in the carbonic acid, as a proof of the existence of oxygen in the carbonic acid. Sometimes we get an awkward piece of potassium that explodes, or something like it, when it burns. I will take another piece; and now that it is heated, I introduce it into the jar, and you perceive that it burns in the carbonic acid—not so well as in the air, because the carbonic acid contains the oxygen combined; but it does burn, and takes away the oxygen. If I now put this potassium into water, I find that, besides the potash formed (which you need not trouble about), there is a quantity of carbon produced. I have here made the experiment in a very rough way; but I assure you that if I were to make it carefully, devoting a day to it, instead of five minutes, we should get all the proper amount of charcoal left in the spoon, or in the place where the potassium was burned, so that there could be no doubt as to the result. Here, then, is the carbon obtained from the carbonic acid, as a common

black substance; so that you have the entire proof of the nature of carbonic acid as consisting of carbon and oxygen. And now, I may tell you, that *whenever* carbon burns under common circumstances, it produces carbonic acid.

Suppose I take this piece of wood, and put it into a bottle with limewater. I might shake that limewater up with wood and the atmosphere as long as I pleased, it would still remain clear as you see it; but suppose I burn the piece of wood in the air of that bottle. You, of course, know I get water. Do I get carbonic acid? There it is, you see—that is to say, the carbonic lime, which results from carbonic acid, and that carbonic acid must be formed from the carbon which comes from the wood, from the candle, or any other thing. Indeed, you have yourselves frequently tried a very pretty experiment, by which you may see the carbon in wood. If you take a piece of wood, and partly burn it, and then blow it out, you have carbon left. There are things that do not show carbon in this way. A candle does not show it, but it contains carbon. Here also is a jar of coal gas, which produces carbonic acid abundantly. You do not see the carbon, but we can soon show it to you. I will light it, and as long as there is any gas in this cylinder it will go on burning. You see

no carbon, but you see a flame; and because that is bright, it will lead you to guess that there is carbon in the flame. But I will show it to you by another process. I have some of the same gas in another vessel, mixed with a body that will burn the hydrogen of the gas, but will not burn the carbon. I will light them with a burning taper, and you perceive the hydrogen is consumed, but not the carbon, which is left behind as a dense black smoke. I hope that by these three or four experiments you will learn to see when carbon is present, and understand what are the products of combustion, when gas or other bodies are thoroughly burned in the air.

Before we leave the subject of carbon, let us make a few experiments and remarks upon its wonderful condition as respects ordinary combustion. I have shown you that the carbon, in burning, burns only as a solid body, and yet you perceive that, after it is burned, it ceases to be a solid. There are very few fuels that act like this. It is, in fact, only that great source of fuel, the carbonaceous series, the coals, charcoals, and woods, that can do it. I do not know that there is any other elementary substance besides carbon that burns with these conditions; and if it had not been so, what would happen to us? Suppose all fuel had been

like iron, which, when it burns, burns into a solid substance. We could not then have such a combustion as you have in this fireplace. Here also is another kind of fuel which burns very well—as well as, if not better than, carbon—so well, indeed, as to take fire of itself when it is in the air, as you see.

This substance is lead [lead pyrophorus][18] and you see how wonderfully combustible it is. It is very much divided, and is like a heap of coals in the fireplace; the air can get to its surface and inside, and so it burns. But why does it not burn in that way now, when it is lying in a mass? Simply because the air cannot get to it. Though it can produce a great heat, the great heat which we want in our furnaces and under our boilers, still that which is produced cannot get away from the portion which remains unburned underneath, and that portion, therefore, is prevented from coming in contact with the atmosphere, and cannot be consumed. How different is that from carbon? Carbon burns just in the same way as this lead does, and so gives an intense fire in the furnace, or wherever you choose to burn it; but then the body produced by its combustion passes away, and the remaining carbon is left clear. I showed you how carbon went on dissolving in the oxygen, leaving

no ash; whereas here we have actually more ash than fuel, for it is heavier by the amount of the oxygen which has united with it. Thus you see the difference between carbon and lead or iron: if we choose iron, which gives so wonderful a result in our application of this fuel, either as light or heat.

If, when the carbon burned, the product went off as a solid body, you would have had the room filled with an opaque substance, as in the case of the phosphorus; but when carbon burns, everything passes up into the atmosphere. It is in a fixed, almost unchangeable condition before the combustion; but afterwards it is in the form of gas, which it is very difficult (though we have succeeded) to produce in a solid or a liquid state.

Now, I must take you to a very interesting part of our subject—to the relation between the combustion of a candle and that living kind of combustion which goes on within us. In every one of us there is a living process of combustion going on very similar to that of a candle; and I must try to make that plain to you. For it is not merely true in a poetical sense—the relation of the life of man to a taper; and if you will follow, I think I can make this clear. In order to make the relation very plain, I have devised a little apparatus which

we can soon build up before you. Here is a board
and a groove cut in it, and I can close the groove
at the top part by a little cover. I can then con-
tinue the groove as a channel by a glass tube at
each end, there being a free passage through the
whole. Suppose I take a taper or candle (we can
now be liberal in our use of the word "candle,"
since we understand what it means), and place it
in one of the tubes; it will go on, you see, burning
very well. You observe that the air which feeds
the flame passes down the tube at one end, then
goes along the horizontal tube, and ascends the
tube at the other end in which the taper is placed.
If I stop the aperture through which the air en-
ters, I stop combustion as you perceive. I stop the
supply of air, and consequently the candle goes
out. But, now, what will you think of this fact?
In a former experiment I showed you the air
going from one burning candle to a second candle.

*If tube B is filled with
air exhaled from the
lungs, instead of pure
fresh air, the flame in
tube A will be
extinguished.*

If I took the air proceeding from another candle, and sent it down by a complicated arrangement into this tube, I should put this burning candle out. But what will you say when I tell you that my breath will put out that candle? I do not mean by blowing at all, but simply that the nature of my breath is such that a candle cannot burn in it. I will now hold my mouth over the aperture, and without blowing the flame in any way, let no air enter the tube but what comes from my mouth. You see the result. I did not blow the candle out. I merely let the air which I expired pass into the aperture, and the result was that the light went out for want of oxygen, and for no other reason. Something or other—namely, my lungs—had taken away the oxygen from the air, and there was no more to supply the combustion of the candle. It is, I think, very pretty to see the time it takes before the bad air which I throw into this part of the apparatus has reached the candle. The candle at first goes on burning, but so soon as the air has had time to reach it, it goes out. And, now, I will show you another experiment, because this is an important part of our philosophy. Here is a jar which contains fresh air, as you can see by the circumstance of a candle or gaslight burning it. I make it close for a little time, and by means of a

When the air in the bottle is inhaled and exhaled back into the jar, it will no longer support combustion.

pipe I get my mouth over it so that I can inhale the air. By putting it over water, in the way that you see, I am able to draw up this air (supposing the cork to be quite tight), take it into my lungs, and throw it back into the jar. We can then examine it, and see the result. You observe, I first take up the air, and then throw it back, as is evident from the ascent and descent of the water; and now, by putting a taper into the air, you will see the state in which it is, by the light being extinguished. Even one inspiration, you see, has completely spoiled this air, so that it is no use my trying to breathe it a second time. Now, you understand the ground of the impropriety of many of the arrangements among the houses of the poorer classes, by which the air is breathed over and over again, for the want of a supply, by means of proper ventilation, sufficient to produce a good result. You see how bad the air becomes by a single

breathing; so that you can easily understand how essential fresh air is to us.

To pursue this a little further, let us seee what will happen with limewater. Here is a globe which contains a little limewater, and it is so arranged as regards the pipes, as to give access to the air within, so that we can ascertain the effect of respired or unrespired air upon it. Of course, I can either draw in air [through *A*], and so make the air that feeds my lungs go through the limewater, or I can force the air out of my lungs through the tube [*B*], which goes to the bottom, and so show its effect upon the limewater. You will observe that, however long I draw the external air into the limewater, and then through it to my lungs, I shall produce no effect upon the water—it will not make the limewater turbid; but if I throw the air *from* my lungs through the limewater, several times in succession, you see how white and milky the water is getting, showing the effect which ex-

Air from the lungs is breathed into the jar through tube B. The limewater becomes milky, showing the presence of carbonic acid in expired air.

pired air has had upon it; and now you begin to
know that the atmosphere which we have spoiled
by respiration is spoiled by carbonic acid, for you
see it here in contact with the limewater.

I have here two bottles, one containing lime-
water and the other common water, and tubes
which pass into the bottles and connect them. The
apparatus is very rough, but it is useful notwith-
standing. If I take these two bottles, inhaling here
and exhaling there, the arrangement of the tubes
will prevent the air going backwards. The air
coming in will go to my mouth and lungs, and in
going out, will pass through the limewater, so that
I can go on breathing and making an experiment,
very refined in its nature, and very good in its
results. You will observe that the good air has
done nothing to the limewater; in the other case
nothing has come to the limewater but my respira-
tion, and you see the difference in the two
cases.

Let us now go a little further. What is all this
process going on within us which we cannot do
without, either day or night, which is so pro-
vided for by the Author of all things that He has
arranged that it shall be independent of all will?
If we restrain our respiration, as we can to a cer-
tain extent, we should destroy ourselves. When we

are asleep, the organs of respiration, and the parts
that are associated with them, still go on with their
action—so necessary is this process of respiration
to us, this contact of the air with the lungs. I
must tell you, in the briefest possible manner,
what this process is. We consume food: the food
goes through that strange set of vessels and organs
within us, and is brought into various parts of the
system, into the digestive parts especially; and
alternately the portion which is so changed is car-
ried through our lungs by one set of vessels, while
the air that we inhale and exhale is drawn into and
thrown out of the lungs by another set of vessels,
so that the air and the food come close together,
separated only by an exceedingly thin surface: the
air can thus act upon the blood by this process,
producing precisely the same results in kind as we
have seen in the case of the candle. The candle
combines with parts of the air, forming carbonic
acid, and evolves heat; so in the lungs there is this
curious, wonderful change taking place. The air
entering, combines with the carbon (not carbon
in a free state, but, as in this case, placed ready for
action at the moment), and makes carbonic acid,
and is so thrown out into the atmosphere, and
thus this singular result takes place: we may thus
look upon the food as fuel. Let me take that piece

of sugar, which will serve my purpose. It is a compound of carbon, hydrogen, and oxygen, similar to a candle, as containing the same elements, though not in the same proportion—the proportions being as shown in this table:

Carbon 72
Hydrogen 11 ⎫
Oxygen 88 ⎭ 99

This is, indeed, a very curious thing, which you can well remember, for the oxygen and hydrogen are in exactly the proportions which form water, so that sugar may be said to be compounded of 72 parts of carbon and 99 parts of water; and it is the carbon in the sugar that combines with the oxygen carried in by the air in the process of respiration—so making us like candles—producing these actions, warmth, and far more wonderful results besides, for the sustenance of the system, by a most beautiful and simple process. To make this still more striking, I will take a little sugar; or, to hasten the experiment, I will use some syrup, which contains about three fourths of sugar and a little water. If I put a little oil of vitriol on it, it takes away the water, and leaves the carbon in a black mass. You see how the carbon is coming out, and before long we shall have a solid mass of char-

coal, all of which has come out of sugar. Sugar, as you know, is food and here we have absolutely a solid lump of carbon where you would not have expected it. And if I make arrangements so as to oxidize the carbon of sugar, we shall have a much more striking result. Here is sugar, and I have here an oxidizer—a quicker one than the atmosphere; and so we shall oxidize this fuel by a process different from respiration in its form, though not different in its kind. It is the combustion of the carbon by the contact of oxygen which the body has supplied to it. If I set this into action at once, you will see combustion produced. Just what occurs in my lungs—taking in oxygen from another source, namely, the atmosphere—takes place here by a more rapid process.

You will be astonished when I tell you what this curious play of carbon amounts to. A candle will burn some four, five, six, or seven hours. What, then, must be the daily amount of carbon going up into the air in the way of carbonic acid! What a quantity of carbon must go from each of us in respiration! What a wonderful change of carbon must take place under these circumstances of combustion or respiration! A man in twenty-four hours converts as much as seven ounces of carbon into carbonic acid; a milch cow will convert

seventy ounces, and a horse seventy-nine ounces, solely by the act of respiration. That is, the horse in twenty-four hours burns seventy-nine ounces of charcoal, or carbon, in his organs of respiration, to supply his natural warmth in that time. All the warm-blooded animals get their warmth in this way, by the conversion of carbon, not in a free state, but in a state of combination. And what an extraordinary notion this gives us of the alterations going on in our atmosphere. As much as 5,000,000 pounds, or 548 tons, of carbonic acid is formed by respiration in London alone in twenty-four hours. And where does all this go? Up into the air. If the carbon had been like the lead which I showed you, or the iron which, in burning, produces a solid substance, what would happen? Combustion could not go on. As charcoal burns, it becomes a vapor and passes off into the atmosphere, which is the great vehicle, the great carrier for conveying it away to other places. Then, what becomes of it? Wonderful is it to find that the change produced by respiration, which seems so injurious to us (for we cannot breathe air twice over), is the very life and support of plants and vegetables that grow upon the surface of the earth. It is the same also under the surface, in the great bodies of water; for fishes and other

animals respire upon the same principle, though not exactly by contact with the open air.

Such fish as I have here respire by the oxygen which is dissolved from the air by the water, and from carbonic acid; and they all move about to produce the one great work of making the animal and vegetable kingdoms subservient to each other. And all the plants growing upon the surface of the earth, like that which I have brought here to serve as an illustration, absorb carbon. These leaves are taking up their carbon from the atmosphere, to which we have given it in the form of carbonic acid, and they are growing and prospering. Give them a pure air like ours, and they could not live in it; give them carbon with other matters, and they live and rejoice. This piece of wood gets all its carbon, as the trees and plants get theirs, from the atmosphere, which, as we have seen, carries away what is bad for us and at the same time good for them—what is disease to the one being health to the other. So are we made dependent, not merely upon our fellow creatures, but upon our fellow existers, all Nature being tied together by the laws that make one part conduce to the good of another.

There is another little point which I must mention before we draw to a close—a point which con-

cerns the whole of these operations, and most curious and beautiful it is to see it clustering upon and associated with the bodies that concern us— oxygen, hydrogen, and carbon, in different states of their existence. I showed you just now some powdered lead, which I set burning,[18] and you saw that the moment the fuel was brought to the air, it acted, even before it got out of the bottle— the moment the air crept in, it acted. Now, there is a case of chemical affinity by which all our operations proceed. When we breathe, the same operation is going on within us. When we burn a candle, the attraction of the different parts one to the other is going on. Here it is going on in this case of the lead; and it is a beautiful instance of chemical affinity. If the products of combustion rose off from the surface, the lead would take fire, and go on burning to the end; but you remember that we have this difference between charcoal and lead—that, while the lead can start into action at once, if there be access of air to it, the carbon will remain days, weeks, months, or years. The manuscripts of Herculaneum were written with carbonaceous ink, and there they have been for 1,800 years or more, not having been at all changed by the atmosphere, though coming in contact with it under various circumstances. Now,

what is the circumstance which makes the lead and carbon differ in this respect? It is a striking thing to see that the matter which is appointed to serve the purpose of fuel *waits* in its action: it does not start off burning, like the lead and many other things that I could show you; but it waits for action. This waiting is a curious and wonderful thing. Candles do not start into action at once, like the lead or iron (for iron finely divided does the same thing as lead), but there they wait for years, perhaps for ages, without undergoing any alteration. I have here a supply of coal gas. The jet is giving forth the gas, but you see it does not take fire—it comes out into the air, but it waits till it is hot enough before it burns. If I make it hot enough, it takes fire. If I blow it out, the gas that is issuing forth waits till the light is applied to it again. It is curious to see how different substances wait—how some will wait till the temperature is raised a little, and others till it is raised a good deal. I have here a little gunpowder and some guncotton; even these things differ in the conditions under which they will burn. The gunpowder is composed of carbon and other substances, making it highly combustible; and the guncotton (nitrocellulose) is another combustible preparation. They are both waiting, but they will start into ac-

tivity at different degrees of heat, or under different conditions. By applying a heated wire to them, we shall see which will start first. You see the gun-cotton has gone off, but not even the hottest part of the wire is now hot enough to fire the gunpowder. How beautifully that shows you the difference in the degree in which bodies act in this way! In the one case the substance will wait any time until the associated bodies are made active by heat; but in the other, as in the process of respiration, it waits no time. In the lungs, as soon as the air enters, it unites with the carbon; even in the lowest temperature which the body can bear short of being frozen, the action begins at once, producing the carbonic acid of respiration: and so all things go on fitly and properly. Thus you see the analogy between respiration and combustion is rendered still more beautiful and striking.

Indeed, all I can say to you at the end of these lectures (for we must come to an end at one time or other) is to express a wish that you may, in your generation, be fit to compare to a candle; that you may, like it, shine as lights to those about you; that, in all your actions, you may justify the beauty of the taper by making your deeds honorable and effectual in the discharge of your duty to your fellow men.

NOTES

(1) The fat or tallow consists of a chemical combination of fatty acids with glycerine. The lime unites with the palmitic, oleic, and stearic acids, and separates the glycerine. After washing, the insoluble lime soap is decomposed with hot dilute sulphuric acid. The melted fatty acids thus rise as an oil to the surface, when they are decanted. They are again washed and cast into thin plates, which, when cold, are placed between layers of coconut matting and submitted to intense hydraulic pressure. In this way the soft oleic acid is squeezed out, while the hard palmitic and stearic acids remain. These are further purified by pressure at a higher temperature and washing in warm dilute sulphuric acid, when they are ready to be made into candles. These acids are harder and whiter than the fats from which they were obtained, while at the same time they are cleaner and most combustible.

(2) A little borax or phosphorus salt is sometimes added, in order to make the ash fusible.

(3) Capillary attraction or repulsion is the cause which determines the ascent or descent of a fluid in a capillary tube. If a piece of thermometer tubing, open at each end, be plunged into water, the latter will instantly rise in the tube considerably above its external level. If, on the other hand, the tube be plunged into mercury, a repulsion instead of attraction will be exhibited, and the level of the mercury will be lower in the tube than it is outside.

(4) The late Duke of Sussex was, we believe, the first to show that a prawn might be washed on this principle. If the

tail, after pulling off the fan part, be placed in a tumbler of water and the head be allowed to hang over the outside, the water will be sucked up the tail by capillary attraction, and will continue to run out through the head until the water in the glass has sunk so low that the tail ceases to dip into it.

(5) The alcohol had chloride of copper dissolved in it: this produces a beautiful green flame.

(6) Lycopodium is a yellowish powder found in the fruit of the club moss (*Lycopodium clavatum*). It is used in fireworks.

(7) Bunsen has calculated that the temperature of the oxyhydrogen blowpipe is 8061° Centigrade. Hydrogen burning in air has a temperature of 3259° C., and coal gas in air, 2350° C.

(8) The following is the action of the sulphuric acid in inflaming the mixture of sulphuret of antimony and chlorate of potassa. A portion of the latter is decomposed by the sulphuric acid into oxide of chlorine, bisulphate of potassa, and perchlorate of potassa. The oxide of chlorine inflames the sulphuret of antimony, which is a combustible body, and the whole mass instantly bursts into flame.

(9) The "air-burner," which is of such value in the laboratory, owes its advantage to this principle. It consists of a cylindrical metal chimney, covered at the top with a piece of rather coarse iron-wire gauze. This is supported over an Argand burner in such a manner that the gas may mix in the chimney with an amount of air sufficient to burn the carbon and hydrogen simultaneously, so that there may be

no separation of carbon in the flame with consequent deposition of soot. The flame, being unable to pass through the wire gauze, burns in a steady, nearly invisible manner above.

(10) Water is in its densest state at a temperature of 39.1° Fahrenheit.

(11) A mixture of salt and pounded ice reduces the temperature from 32° F. to zero—the ice at the same time becoming fluid.

(12) Potassium, the metallic basis of potash, was discovered in 1807 by Sir Humphry Davy, who succeeded in separating it from potash by means of a powerful voltaic battery. Its great affinity for oxygen causes it to decompose water with evolution of hydrogen, which takes fire with the heat produced.

(13) Professor Faraday has calculated that there is as much electricity required to decompose one grain of water as there is in a very powerful flash of lightning.

(14) A solution of acetate of lead, submitted to the action of the voltaic current, yields lead at the negative pole, and brown peroxide of lead at the positive pole. A solution of nitrate of silver, under the same circumstances, yields silver at the negative pole, and peroxide of silver at the positive pole.

(15) The gas which is thus employed as a test for the presence of oxygen, is the binoxide of nitrogen, or nitrous oxide. It is a colorless gas, which, when brought in contact with oxygen, unites with it, forming hyponitric acid, the red gas referred to.

(16) Carbonic acid gas, or carbon dioxide.

(17) Marble is a compound of carbonic acid and lime. The muriatic acid, being the stronger of the two, takes the place of the carbonic acid, which escapes as a gas, the residue forming muriate of lime or chloride of calcium.

(18) Lead pyrophorus is made by heating dry tartrate of lead in a glass tube (closed at one end, and drawn out to a fine point at the other) until no more vapors are evolved. The open end of the tube is then to be sealed before the blowpipe. When the tube is broken and the contents shaken out into the air, they burn with a red flash.

INDEX